My **BIG** Book of
MATHS and **ENGLISH**

Ages 5–7

Written by
Peter Patilla
Paul Broadbent
Betty Root
Monica Hughes

Gold Stars ®

Helping your child

⭐ Do talk about what's on the page. Let your child know that you are sharing the activities.

⭐ Explain what has to be done on each page, and help with any recording such as colouring and joining up.

⭐ Do not become anxious if your child finds any of the activities too difficult. Young children develop and learn at different rates.

⭐ Let your child do as much or as little as he or she wishes. Do leave a page that seems to be difficult and return to it later.

⭐ It does not matter if your child does some of the pages out of turn.

⭐ The answers to the activities start on page 232.

⭐ Always be encouraging, and give plenty of praise.

⭐ Remember that the gold stars are a reward for effort as well as achievement.

Illustrated by Adam Linley

This is a Parragon book
This edition published in 2006

Parragon
Queen Street House
4 Queen Street
BATH, BA1 1HE, UK

Copyright © Parragon Books Ltd 2002

ISBN 1-40547-616-8
Printed in Malaysia

Contents

Contents

Contents

Contents

Contents

Numbers for counting

Write the numbers. Join each picture to the right number. Join each word to the right number.

four

one

two

five

three

I am the best!

Note for parent: With this activity you will find out if your child can recognize the numbers 1 to 10.

Counting

Count the spots on each dog.
Write the number in the box.

8

10

6

P

2

4

Join the frogs that have the
same number of spots.

Note for parent: This activity give
counting skills in different ways.

I'm a star!

Each frog needs 10 spots.
Draw in the missing spots.

Join the pairs of dogs. Each pair must
have a total of 10 spots.

Easy
Peasy!

Starting to add

Write in the missing numbers.

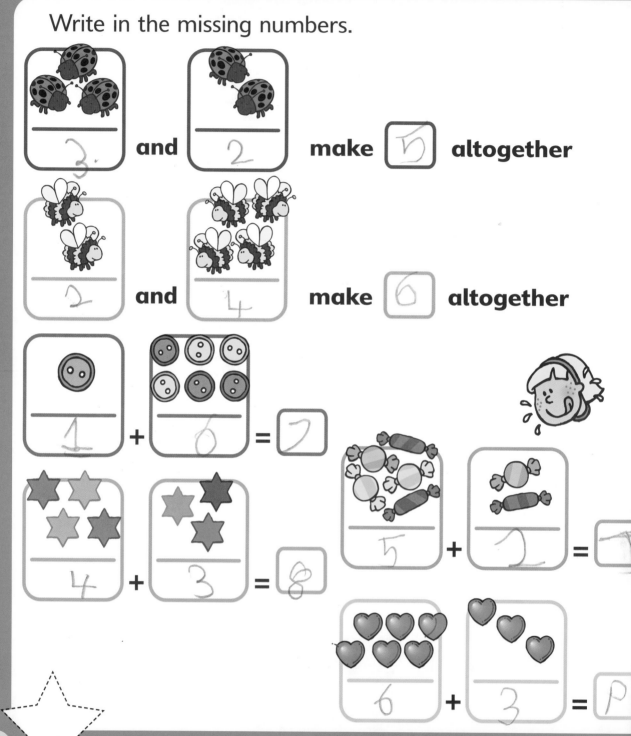

_3_ **and** _2_ **make** _5_ **altogether**

_2_ **and** _4_ **make** _6_ **altogether**

_1_ + _6_ = _7_

_4_ + _3_ = _8_

_5_ + _1_ = _7_

_6_ + _3_ = _P_

Note for parent: In this activity your child is adding pictures, rather than just numbers.

Draw the missing socks above each arrow.

$1 + 4 = 5$

$2 + 3 = 5$

$3 + 4 = 7$

$4 + 3 = 7$

Write the missing numbers.

$3 + 5 = 8$

$4 + 4 = 8$

$1 + 5 = 6$

$2 + 5 = 7$

15

Starting to take away

Dino the Dinosaur eats 2 of everything he sees.
Cross out how many pieces of food Dino eats.
Write how many are left after Dino has eaten.

4 take away **2**

leaves **2**

7 take away **2**

leaves **5**

5 take away **2**

leaves **3**

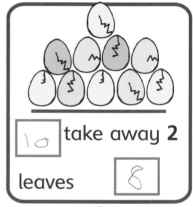

8 take away **2**

leaves **6**

7 take away **2**

leaves **5**

10 take away **2**

leaves **8**

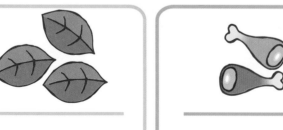

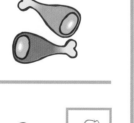

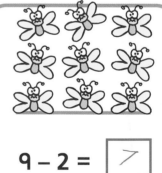

3 – 2 = **1**

2 – 2 = **0**

9 – 2 = **7**

Note for parent: Taking away is the start to learning about subtraction.

How many fish has Charlie Cat eaten from each bowl? Join each START bowl to the correct FINISH bowl.

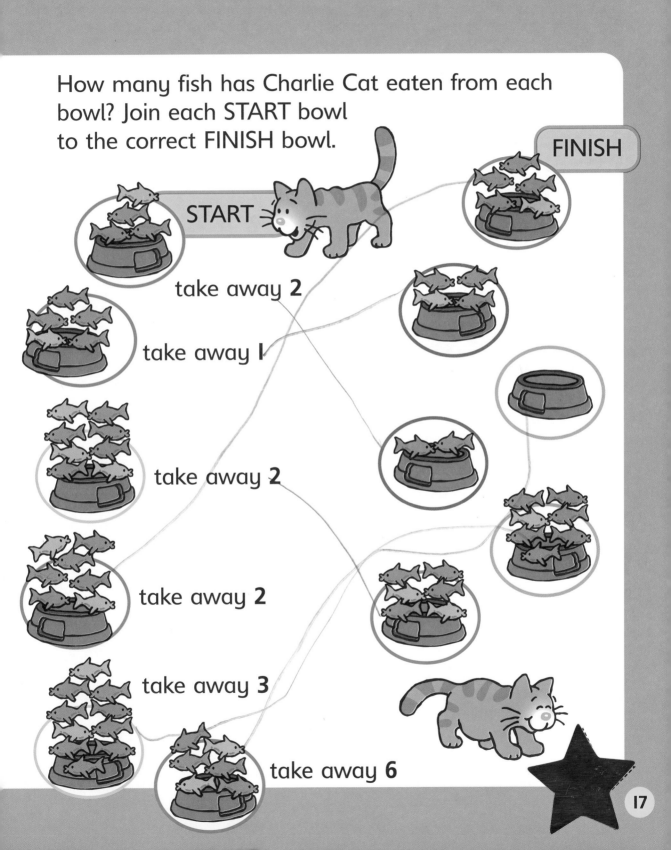

FINISH

START

take away **2**

take away **I**

take away **2**

take away **2**

take away **3**

take away **6**

Looking at shapes

Some of these foods are whole and some have been cut up into pieces. Join each whole to a cut-up piece.

Note for parent: This activity encourages your child to examine shapes closely.

Matching shapes

Colour the matching shapes.

 colour red colour green

 colour blue colour orange

 Note for parent: This activity gives further practice in examining shapes closely.

Solid shapes

Join each set of shapes to its name.

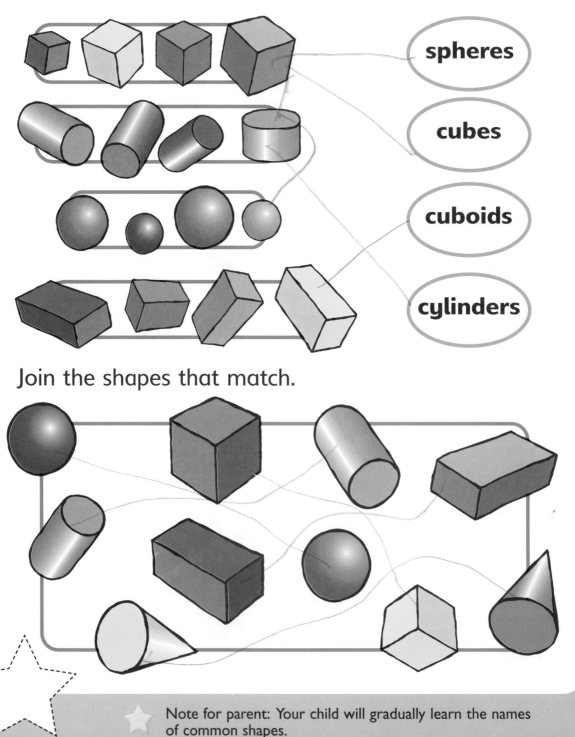

spheres

cubes

cuboids

cylinders

Join the shapes that match.

Note for parent: Your child will gradually learn the names of common shapes.

Second chance

Join each START food to the correct FINISH food.

 START

FINISH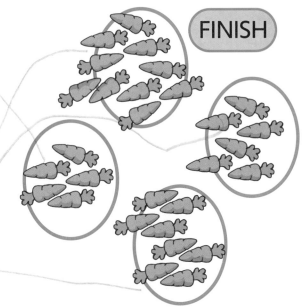

 add on 0

 add on 3

 add on 6

 add on 6

 START

Join each START group to the correct FINISH group.

FINISH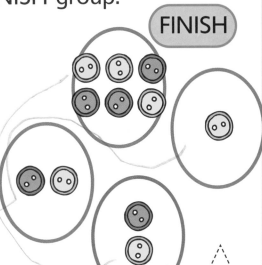

take away 3

 take away 2

take away 0

take away 5

 Note for parent: This activity helps children to remember about adding and taking away.

21

All about halves

Colour half of each shape.

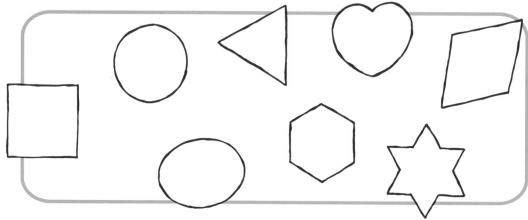

Draw the missing half of each shape.
Join the complete shape to its name.

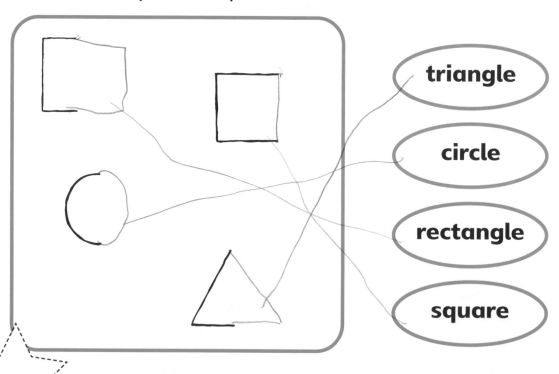

triangle

circle

rectangle

square

Note for parent: Learning about half and fair shares is
important in mathematics.

Colour half of the items in each container.

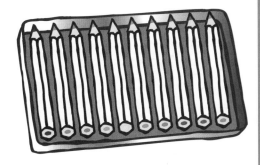

Some marbles are put into two bags.
Put a tick (✔) if the sharing is fair.
Put a cross (✗) if the sharing is not fair.

Adding

Draw in the extra crayons.
Write the total number of crayons.

 I add 4  $1 + 4 = 5$

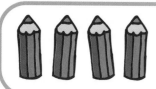 3 add 3 $3 + 3 = 6$

4 add 6 $4 + 6 = 10$

There should be 10 cherries on each plate. Draw the missing cherries.

 $4 + 6 = 10$

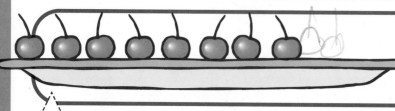 $8 + 2 = 10$

Note for parent: Your child may need to use the number track on page 25 to complete these additions.

Use the number track to help you.
Write how many beads are on each necklace.

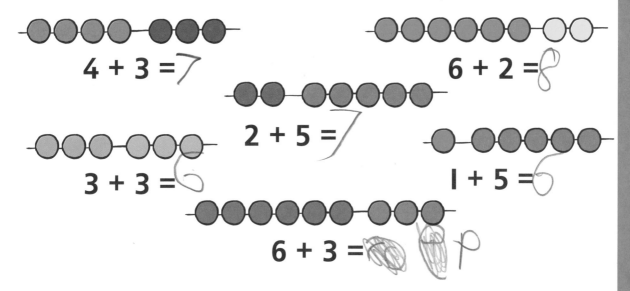

4 + 3 = 7

6 + 2 = 8

2 + 5 = 7

3 + 3 = 6

1 + 5 = 6

6 + 3 =

Join the scarves that have the same total.

1 + 5

8 + 2

5 + 2

4 + 6

4 + 3

3 + 1

2 + 2

3 + 3

I am the best!

25

Subtracting

Cross out the animals to be taken away.
Write how many are left.

4 take away **2**

$4 - 2 = 2$

7 take away **3**

$7 - 3 = 4$

8 take away **5**

$8 - 5 = 3$

Only 3 rockets are needed. Cross off how many
have to be taken away. Write the answer.

$5 - 2 = 3$

$7 - 4 = 3$

Note for parent: Your child may need to use the number
track on page 27 to complete these subtractions.

Use the number track to help you answer the subtractions.

4 – 1 = 3

5 – 3 = 2

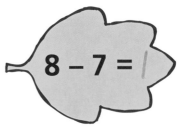
8 – 7 = 1

5 – 5 = 0

9 – 5 = 4

10 – 2 = 8

Join the stars that have the same answer.

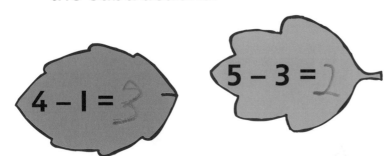
10 – 5

8 – 7

5 – 0

10 – 7

6 – 3

6 – 5

Flat shapes

Cross out the odd one out in each ring.

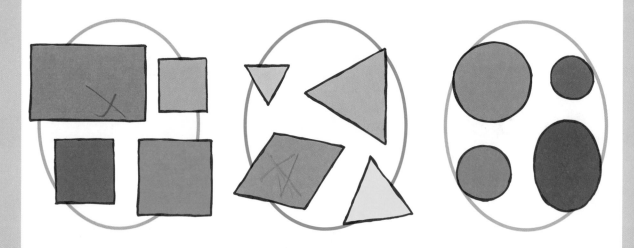

Tick all the shapes that are the same in each row.

Note for parent: This activity gives children useful practice in recognizing shapes.

Sets and pairs

Join each set of shapes to its name.

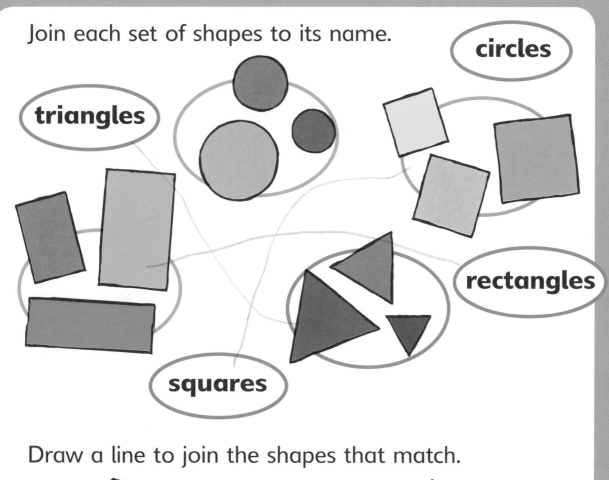

circles

triangles

rectangles

squares

Draw a line to join the shapes that match.

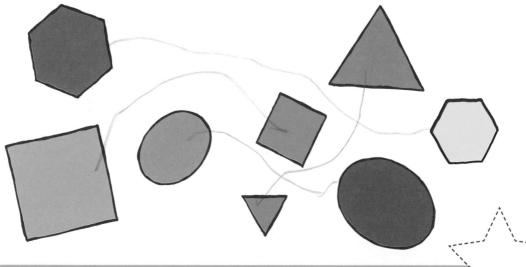

 Note for parent: Gradually your child should learn the names of common shapes.

Time

Write in the missing numbers on the clock.

Write the times under each clock.

__11__ o'clock

__8__ o'clock

__5__ o'clock

Note for parent: This activity will help your child to start recognizing simple times.

Look at the times. Draw in the missing hands.

half-past 3

half-past 8

half-past 12

Write the times under each clock.

half-past _____

half-past _____

half-past _____

Measuring

Draw a longer worm.

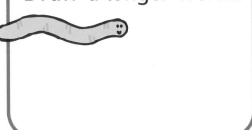

Draw a bigger flower.

Draw a taller rocket.

Draw a shorter lamp post.

Join up the pictures in order of size.
Start with the smallest.

Note for parent: In this activity your child is learning to compare measurements.

Second chance

Use the number track to help you write the answers.

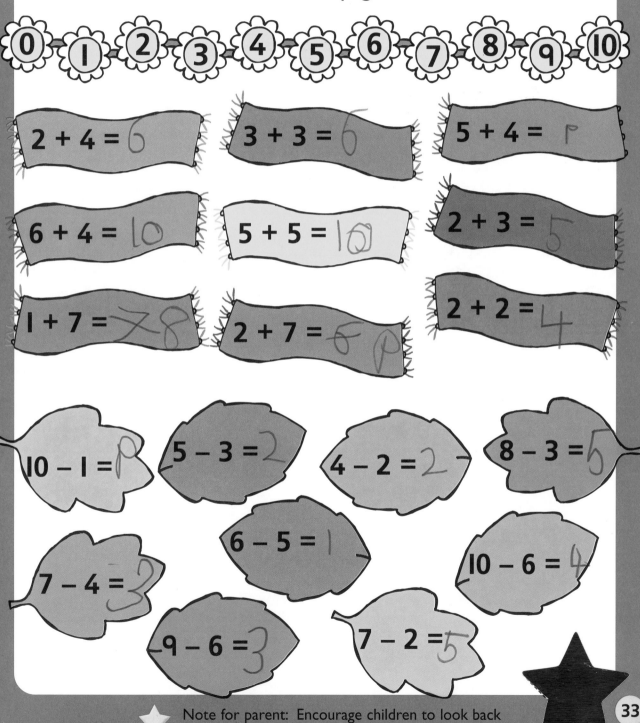

0 1 2 3 4 5 6 7 8 9 10

2 + 4 = 6

3 + 3 = 6

5 + 4 = 9

6 + 4 = 10

5 + 5 = 10

2 + 3 = 5

1 + 7 = 8

2 + 7 = 9

2 + 2 = 4

10 – 1 = 9

5 – 3 = 2

4 – 2 = 2

8 – 3 = 5

7 – 4 = 3

6 – 5 = 1

10 – 6 = 4

9 – 6 = 3

7 – 2 = 5

33

Counting to 20

Write in the missing numbers.

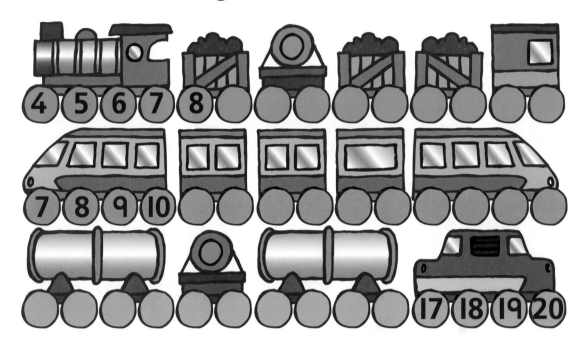

4 5 6 7 8

7 8 9 10

17 18 19 20

Join each word to a number.

12   16

    eleven | twenty

15 fourteen | sixteen 20

11 twelve | thirteen 17

    fifteen | seventeen

14   13

Note for parent: This activity gives your child practice in counting to 20, and in recognizing numbers and words.

Join the dots

Join the dots in order.
Can you name the mystery animals?

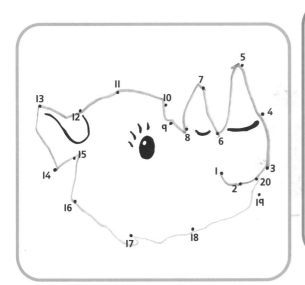

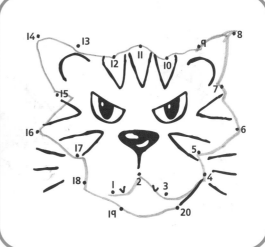

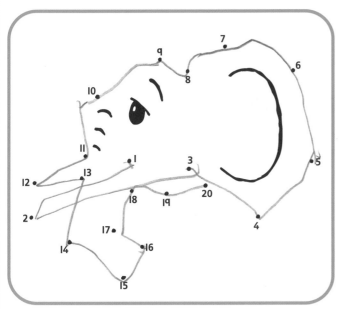

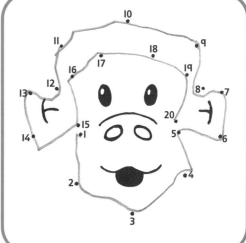

Note for parent: This activity gives further practice in counting up to 20.

Counting on and back

Use the number line to help you count on.
Join each monster to its correct answer on the line.

8 + 3

9 + 5

8 + 7

6 + 7

9 + 9

6 + 4

0 1 2 3 4 5 6 7 8 9 10 11 12 13 14 15 16 17 18 19 20

10 + 3

10 + 5

10 + 8

10 + 6

10 + 10

10 + 1

Note for parent: This activity will help your child to use a
number line to count on and back.

Use the number line to help you
count back. Join each spaceship to
its correct answer on the line.

12 – 8

12 – 6

13 – 4

11 – 9

16 – 8

12 – 5

0 1 2 3 4 5 6 7 8 9 10 11 12 13 14 15 16 17 18 19 20

20 – 4

20 – 5

20 – 6

20 – 8

20 – 2

20 – 7

All about me

Fill in the missing words.

My name is _____

My age is _____

I live at _____

_____

_____

My school is called _____

 My favourite animal is _____

My favourite sport is _____

 Note for parent: Giving information is a useful skill.

Draw yourself in the box.
Read the words and draw a line to the right part.

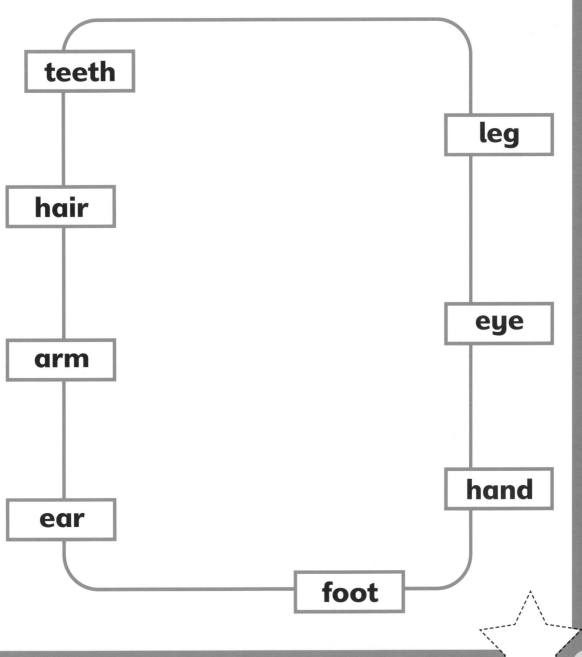

teeth

leg

hair

arm

eye

ear

hand

foot

Note for parent: This activity helps with understanding
parts of the body.

Middle sounds

Join the pictures that have the same middle sounds – **a**, **e**, **i**, **o** or **u**.

Note for parent: Children have to listen very carefully to hear middle sounds. Be patient!

Middle vowels

Use the vowels **a**, **e**, **i**, **o** or **u** to complete the words below.

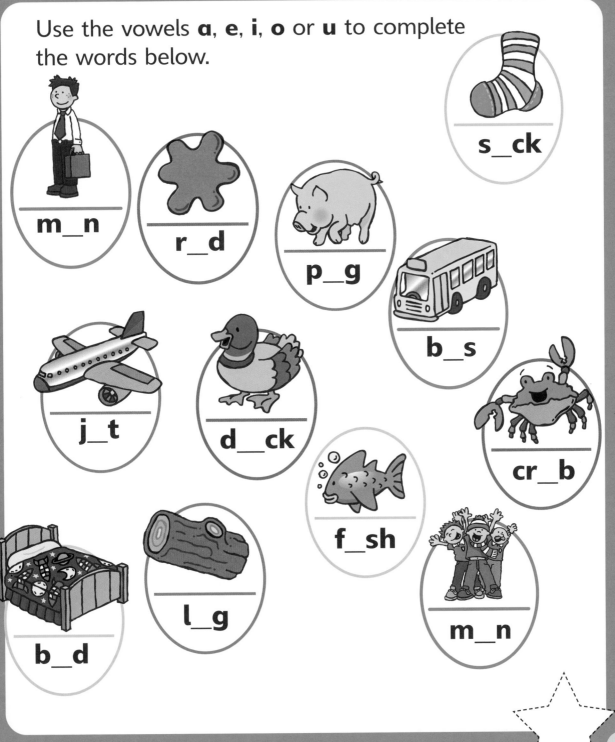

s__ck

m__n

r__d

p__g

b__s

j__t

d__ck

cr__b

f__sh

b__d

l__g

m__n

Note for parent: This activity gives children extra practice in identifying middle sounds.

Odd one out

Cross out the picture in each row that does not belong.

Note for parent: This activity helps children to classify objects.

Silly or sensible?

Look at the picture. Read the sentences and put a tick next to the ones that are sensible.

The teacher is under the table. ___
A girl is reading a book. ___
A boy is painting the door. ___
The teacher is looking at the children. ___
A cat is reading a book. ___
A boy has got a brush. ___
The hamster is on its cage. ___

 Note for parent: This activity helps children to understand sentences and make the correct response.

Using labels

Read these words:

ball   boy   girl   man   car   tree

Now write the words in the boxes below.

Note for parent: This activity gives practice with reading
words and placing them in the correct context.

The alphabet

Write in the missing letters. Some are capital letters and some are lower-case ones.
Draw your own pictures in the empty squares.

Note for parent: This activity helps with capital letters and beginning sounds.

Double sounds

Look at these pictures and say each beginning sound.

bl   br   cl   cr

Fill in the missing letters.

_ _ock   _ _idge   _ _own   _ _ack

Now do the same again.

dr   fl   gr   pl

_ _een   _ _ug   _ _ill   _ _ag

Note for parent: This activity helps children to learn these double beginning sounds: bl, br, cl, cr, dr, fl, gr and pl.

Beginning sounds

Look at the first picture in each row.
Tick the other pictures in the same row
that start in the same way.

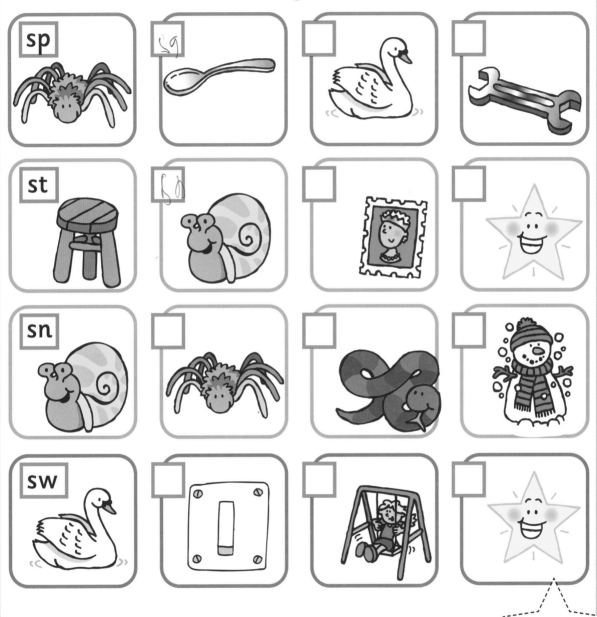

Note for parent: This activity helps children to learn
these double beginning sounds: sp, st, sn and sw.

Second chance

Join the sounds to the pictures.

cl

dr

sn

bl

gr

sp

st

sw

Note for parent: Here is a second chance to remember
double sounds.

Read and draw

Read the sentences and finish the picture.

Draw a tree <u>by</u> the river.
Draw a boat going <u>under</u> the bridge.
Draw a duck <u>on</u> the river.
Draw a car going <u>over</u> the bridge.
Draw yourself climbing <u>up</u> the tree.

 Note for parent: This activity helps children to learn positional words such as by, under, on, over and up.

The Enormous Turnip

Look at the pictures. Read the sentences.
Match each sentence to the correct picture.

Everyone fell over and the turnip came out. __

The farmer saw an enormous turnip. __

Everyone tried to pull up the turnip. __

The farmer tried to pull up the turnip. __

Note for parent: This activity gives practice in reading for understanding.

How does it end?

Look at each row of pictures. Tell the story but choose the ending that you like the best.

or

Note for parent: This activity gives children practice in telling a story from pictures.

Alphabetical order

a b c d e f g h i j k l m n o p q r s t u v w x y z

Write the beginning sound of each picture.
Then put the three letters in each row in
alphabetical order.

Note for parent: Two skills are required for this activity:
knowing beginning sounds and alphabetical order.

Little words

Find each little word in one of the big words and then join them with a line.

or

us

an

all

am

in

at

fork

lamb

twins

bat

man

ball

bus

How many of the little words can you read? _____

Note for parent: It is great fun to find words inside other words.

Find the right word

sun   bed   boy   ball   girl   tree

Choose one of these words to complete each of the sentences.

A little **girl** put on her dress.

The _____ was hot.

I like getting into my _____ to go to sleep.

I can see a bird's nest in the _____ .

Dad kicked the _____ .

A little _____ put on his football boots.

Note for parent: This activity helps children to read and understand key words.

Making sentences

These sentences are all muddled. Write them in the right order and then finish each one with a full stop . or a question mark ?

is time What the

_____

chips I to like eat

_____

do go school When I to

_____

car going The was fast

_____

up Who the with went Jill hill

_____

on lap The likes sit to my cat

_____

How many capital letters can you count?_____

 Note for parent: This activity gives practice with sorting words to make sense and using punctuation.

55

Alphabetical order

Look at the names and then write them in the register in the correct order. Remember the capital letters.

Imran

Alison

Jamilla

Meena

Class Register

Alison

_____

_____

_____

_____

_____

_____

Wendy

Duncan

Samuel

Patrick

Wendy

Note for parent: This activity helps children to practise using alphabetical order for a familiar situation.

Days of the week

Look at the pictures. Read the questions and then write the correct day. Remember the capital letters.

 Clare

 Jack

Monday

Friday

On which day does Clare go trampolining? _____

On which day does Clare watch television?

_____

Tuesday

On which day does Jack go to the library? _____

Saturday

On which day does Clare go shopping? _____

On which day does Jack wash the car? _____

Wednesday

Sunday

On which day does Clare take the dog out? _____

On which day does Jack play football?_____

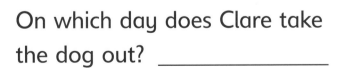
Thursday

 Note for parent: This activity helps children to learn to read the days of the week.

57

Find your way

Read these instructions. Draw the correct way from the house to the school.

Start at ✘

Walk down the path and turn right out of the gate.

Turn right again past some trees.

Walk along the path to the traffic lights.

Cross the road when it is safe.

Turn right and then turn left into **School Road**.

Go past the fence and turn left through the school gate.

Note for parent: This activity helps children to read instructions and follow them.

Telephone numbers

Use this telephone directory to answer the questions at the bottom of the page.

Mr Anderson	9802	*Mr Mead*	9980
Mr Caswell	9146	*Miss Palmer*	9544
Mrs Depster	9829	*Mr Shah*	9827
Miss Heelan	9026	*Mrs Todd*	9412
Ms Kamara	9530	*Ms Walker*	9361

What is Mr Shah's number? _____

What is Miss Heelan's number? _____

What is Mr Caswell's number? _____

What is Miss Palmer's number? _____

Whose number is 9361? _____

Whose number is 9802? _____

Whose number is 9412? _____

Whose number is 9829? _____

Do you know your own
telephone number at home? _____

Note for parent: This activity helps children to
learn how to use lists of numbers.

Animal dictionary

Match each word to the correct meaning.
Draw a line to join them.

elephant

kangaroo

monkey

panda

zebra

A large animal that can jump very well. It carries its young in a pouch. It comes from Australia.

A small animal with long arms and feet that it uses like hands. It lives in jungles.

A large animal with a long trunk and ivory tusks. It lives in Africa and Asia.

An animal like a horse with black and white stripes. It lives in Africa.

A black and white animal like a bear. It lives in China.

60

Reading an index

Use the index below to answer the questions at the bottom of the page.

Index

Apes	10	Kangaroos	20
Bears	8	Monkeys	6
Chimpanzees	14	Penguins	28
Crocodiles	22	Sharks	4
Dolphins	26	Turtles	12
Giraffes	18	Whales	16

Page 18 is about _____

Page 28 is about _____

Page 16 is about _____

Page 8 is about _____

Page 12 is about _____

Apes are on page _____

Sharks are on page _____

Kangaroos are on page _____

Giraffes are on page _____

Chimpanzees are on page _____

Which page would you like to read? _____

Why? _____

Second chance

Write the first two letters.

Join two pictures that start in the same way.

Note for parent: This page gives children a chance to remember what they have learned.

Making lists

Write the words in the correct lists.

spade

Things I use in the kitchen	Things I use in the garden

pan

knife

wheelbarrow

watering can

spoon

frying pan

fork

food processor

lawnmower

Note for parent: This activity gives children practice with sorting things into lists.

Patterns in words

Make two more words by adding one letter.

ball   **_all**   **_all**

Write a sentence with each of the two words you have made.

1._____

2._____

Now do the same again.

man   **_an**   **_an**

hat   **_at**   **_at**

1._____

2._____

1._____

2._____

Note for parent: This activity encourages children to look for patterns in words.

Find the rhymes

Colour in blue the words that rhyme with **take**.
Colour in green the words that rhyme with **ball**.
Colour in red the words that rhyme with **shell**.
Colour in yellow the words that rhyme with **pin**.

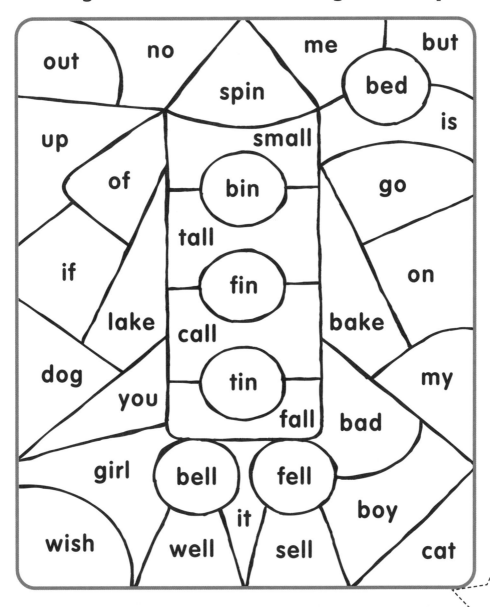

out   no   me   but

spin   bed

up   small   is

of   bin   go

tall

if   fin   on

lake   bake

call

dog   tin   my

you   fall   bad

girl   bell   fell   boy

it

wish   well   sell   cat

 Note for parent: This activity helps children to see patterns and to hear rhymes in words.

Numbers to 10

Trace the numbers. Join each kite to the right number. Join each number to the right group of pictures at the bottom of each page.

one

two

three

four

five

1 2 3 4 5

Note for parent: Ask your child to say each number and word aloud as he or she traces over them.

six seven eight nine ten

6 7 8 9 10

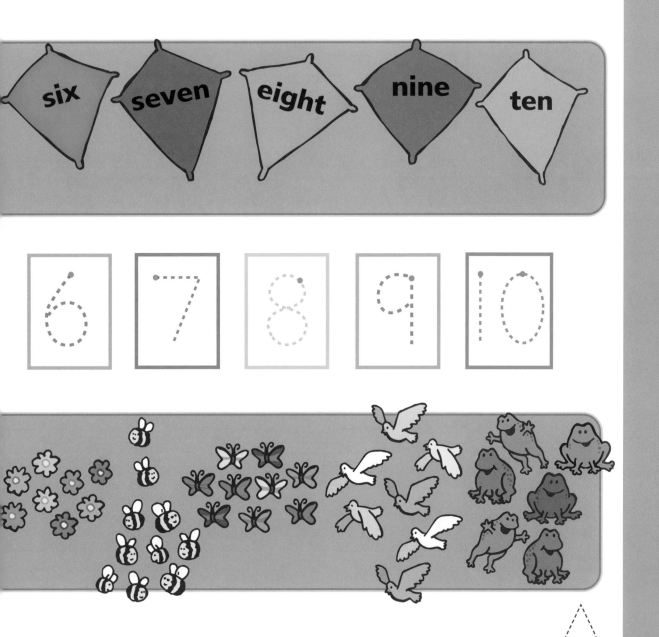

Counting

Count the objects in the big picture.
Write the correct number in each box.

Note for parent: To help find the totals, children can
mark each object as they count.

Comparing

Colour most spaceships red. Colour the rest of the spaceships blue. Write the numbers in the boxes.

	red spaceships
	blue spaceships

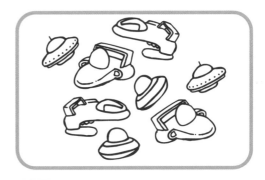

	red spaceships
	blue spaceships

	red spaceships
	blue spaceships
	spaceships altogether

	red spaceships
	blue spaceships
	spaceships altogether

Note for parent: Your child chooses how many to colour red – there must be more red spaceships than blue ones.

69

Putting together

Count each set. Write how many there are altogether.

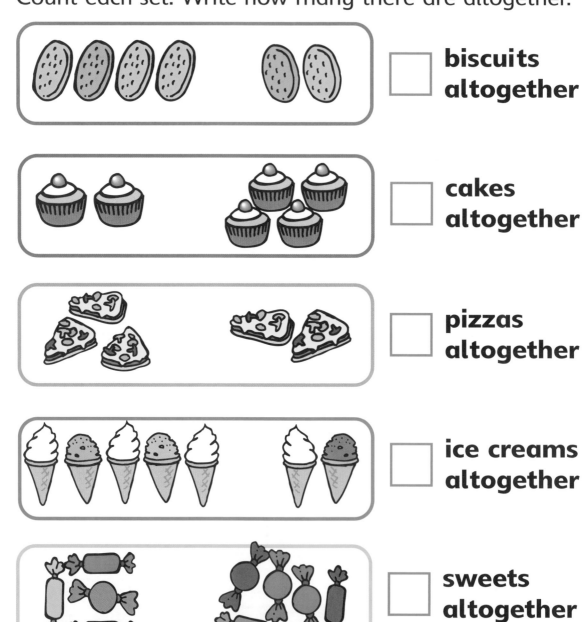

biscuits altogether

cakes altogether

pizzas altogether

ice creams altogether

sweets altogether

Note for parent: Encourage your child to count on from the first number to find the total.

Count the spots on each monster.
How many spots are there altogether?

⬜ **and** ⬜ **make** ⬜ **altogether**

⬜ **and** ⬜ **make** ⬜ **altogether**

⬜ **and** ⬜ **make** ⬜ **altogether**

How many are left?

Cross out two in each set. Write how many are left.

| 5 | take away | 2 |

leaves ☐

| 6 | take away | 2 |

leaves ☐

| 8 | take away | 2 |

leaves ☐

| 4 | take away | 2 |

leaves ☐

Some birds are flying away.
How many are left on the branch?

| 9 | take away | 3 | leaves ☐

Note for parent: This activity will help your child to
recognize numbers and match them to an amount.

Finding differences

How many more children are there than chairs?

☐ **children**

☐ **chairs**

difference ➜ ☐

☐ **children**

☐ **chairs**

difference ➜ ☐

☐ **children**

☐ **chairs**

difference ➜ ☐

Note for parent: Finding the difference is the same as counting on from the smaller number to the larger one.

Number machines

Sweets go into these adding machines.
Write how many come out of each machine.

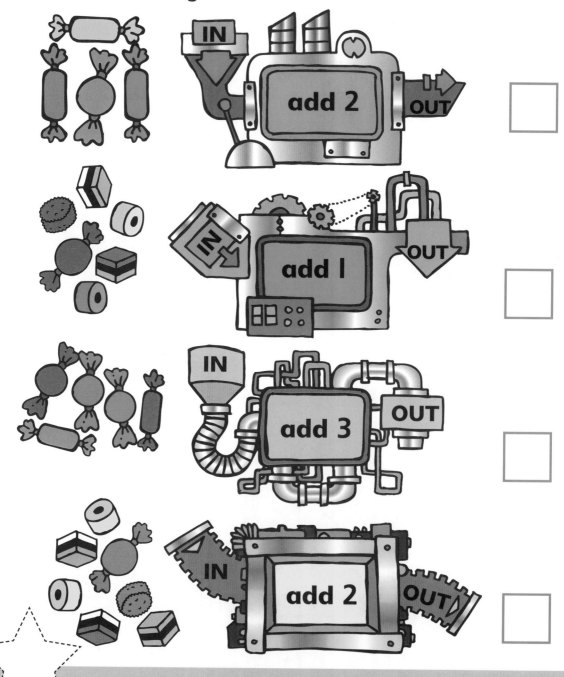

Note for parent: Encourage your child to count on from the IN number for adding, and to count back for taking away.

Drinks go into these take-away machines.
Write how many come out of each machine.

Second chance

Count each set. Write how many there are altogether.

☐ **biscuits altogether**

☐ **cakes altogether**

Count the spots on each monster.
How many are there altogether?

☐ **and** ☐ **make** ☐ **altogether**

Cross out two in each set. Write how many are left.

| 8 | take away | 2 |

leaves ☐

| 4 | take away | 2 |

leaves ☐

Note for parent: This page helps to find out what
your child can remember.

Hidden numbers

There are 9 rabbits in each line.
Write how many are hidden.

Note for parent: Children need to count the rabbits they can see, then count on to 9 to find the difference.

Adding

Draw the extra balloons in each row.
Write the correct totals.

 **2 add 3**   2 + 3 = ☐

 **3 add 4**   3 + 4 = ☐

 **4 add 5**   4 + 5 = ☐

Write how many there are altogether.

☐ + ☐ = ☐

☐ + ☐ = ☐

Note for parent: Make sure your child recognizes
the addition sign (+) and the equal sign (=).

Write how many coloured pencils there are altogether.

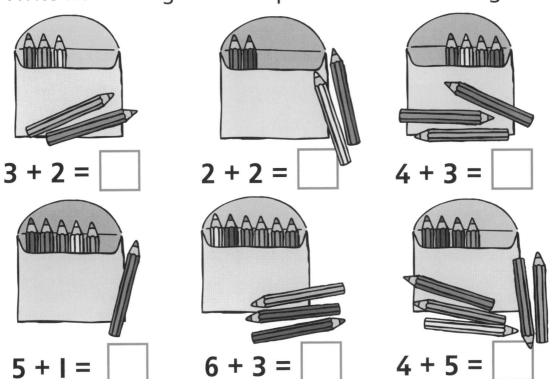

3 + 2 = ☐

2 + 2 = ☐

4 + 3 = ☐

5 + 1 = ☐

6 + 3 = ☐

4 + 5 = ☐

Join each sum to the correct total.

5+2   3+3   4+1   1+3   4+4

5   8   6   7   4

Taking away

Two children get out of each of these trains.
How many are left on each train?

7 take away 2 is ⬚   **7 – 2 =** ⬚

5 take away 2 is ⬚   **5 – 2 =** ⬚

8 take away 2 is ⬚   **8 – 2 =** ⬚

Cross out some flags. Write how many are left.

9 – ⬚ **is** ⬚

Note for parent: Make sure your child recognizes the subtraction sign (–). Remember to use the words 'subtract' and 'take away'.

Draw how many balls come out of the machines. Write the totals in the red boxes.

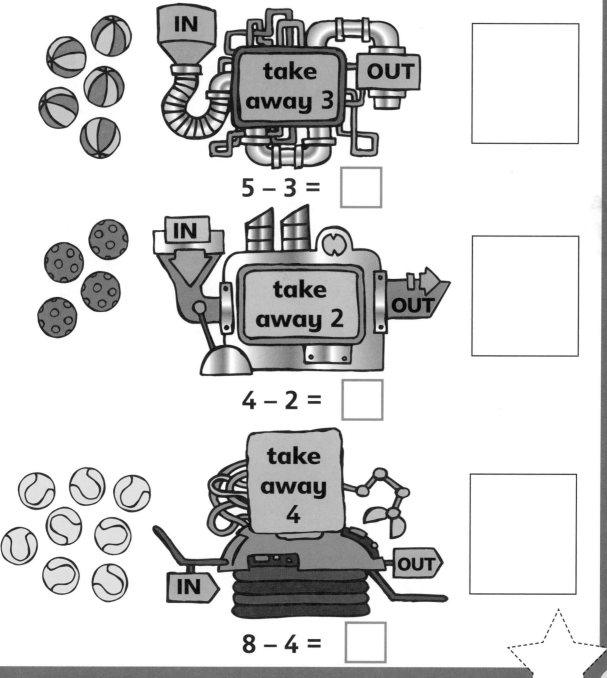

5 − 3 =

4 − 2 =

8 − 4 =

Counting on

Use the number track to count on. Show the jumps and write the answer. The first one has been done for you.

$4 + 2 = \boxed{6}$ 1 2 3 4 5 6 7 8 9 10

$5 + 3 = \boxed{}$ 1 2 3 4 5 6 7 8 9 10

$7 + 2 = \boxed{}$ 1 2 3 4 5 6 7 8 9 10

$3 + 4 = \boxed{}$ 1 2 3 4 5 6 7 8 9 10

$6 + 4 = \boxed{}$ 1 2 3 4 5 6 7 8 9 10

$2 + 3 = \boxed{}$ 1 2 3 4 5 6 7 8 9 10

Note for parent: These activities will help your child to use a number track or number line to count on to find a total.

Join each rocket to the correct answer on the number line.

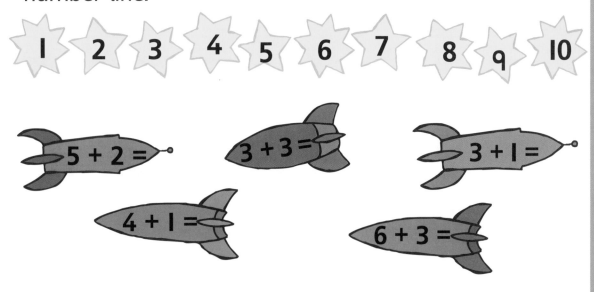

Write the missing numbers in these counting patterns.

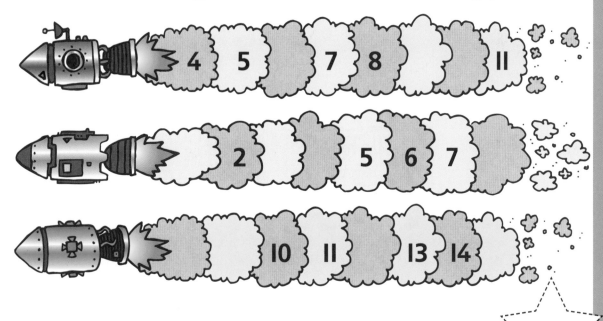

Counting back

Use the number line to count back. Show the jumps and write the answer.

6 − 3 = ☐

5 − 2 = ☐

8 − 4 = ☐

9 − 3 = ☐

10 − 2 = ☐

7 − 6 = ☐

Note for parent: Counting back on a number line or number track is a good method for taking away.

Work out each answer. Colour the correct number in the number track to match.

Addition bonds

Make these totals in different ways.
Write the answers in the boxes.

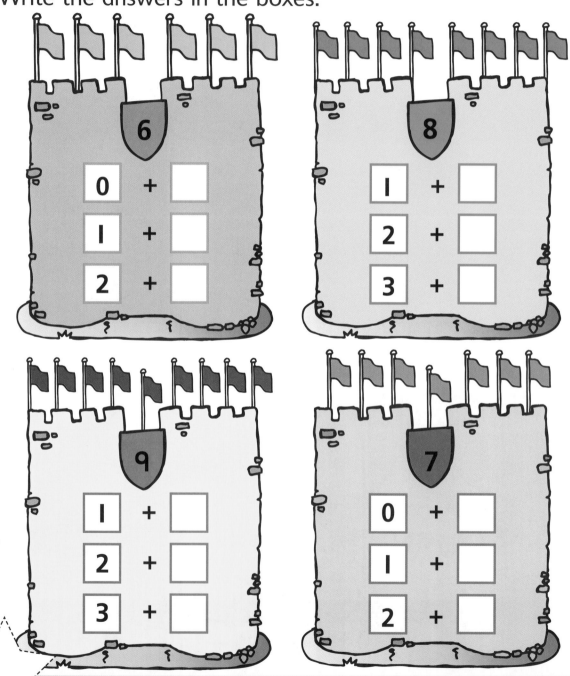

6

0 + ☐
1 + ☐
2 + ☐

8

1 + ☐
2 + ☐
3 + ☐

9

1 + ☐
2 + ☐
3 + ☐

7

0 + ☐
1 + ☐
2 + ☐

Note for parent: Addition bonds are all the different ways that a total can be made by adding two numbers.

Draw a line from each flower to the pot with the correct total.

What can you see if you colour all the shapes with a total of 10?

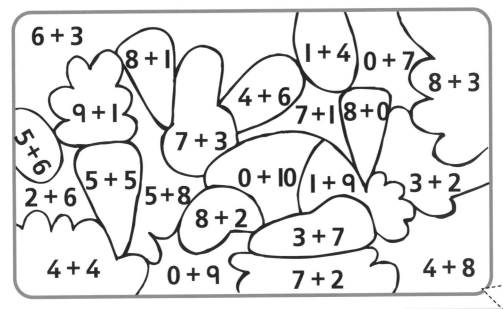

Subtraction bonds

Find different ways of making 3 and 4.

3

4 – 1
7 –
3 –
9 –
8 –

4

7 –
5 –
9 –
8 –
6 –

Find different ways to make the answer of 5 .

Note for parent: These activities will help your child to learn the subtraction bonds up to 10.

Second chance

Join the sums to the correct totals.

Draw how many balls come out of the machines.

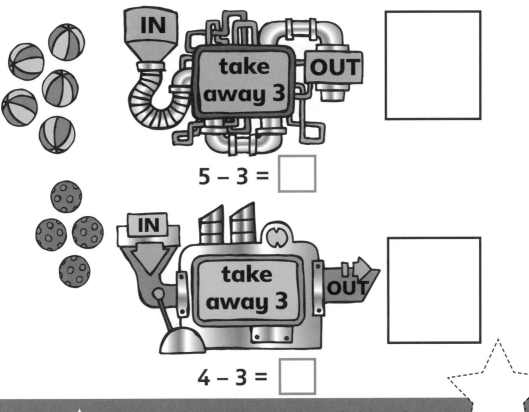

$5 - 3 =$ ☐

$4 - 3 =$ ☐

Note for parent: This page helps to find out what your child can remember.

Addition facts

Write the answers in the boxes. Use the number track to help you.

4 + 3 = ☐   6 + 2 = ☐   5 + 5 = ☐

9 + 1 = ☐   7 + 2 = ☐   3 + 5 = ☐

2 + 4 = ☐   4 + 4 = ☐   6 + 3 = ☐

The top can is the total of the two cans below. Write the missing numbers. The first one has been done for you.

Write the missing numbers.

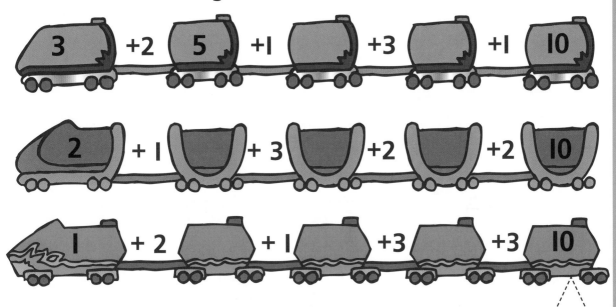

+ 3 = 7

+ 2 = 5

4 + = 9

6 + = 9

+ 8 = 10

5 + = 8

+ 2 = 8

3 + = 6

+ 7 = 10

Follow these trails to reach 10.
Write the missing totals.

3   +2   5   +1   ___   +3   ___   +1   10

2   + 1   ___   + 3   ___   +2   ___   +2   10

1   + 2   ___   + 1   ___   +3   ___   +3   10

Subtraction facts

Write the answers in the boxes. Use the
number track to help you.

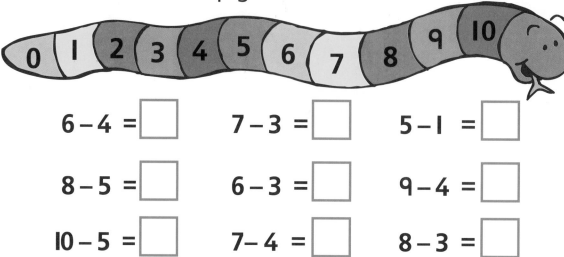

6 − 4 = ☐   7 − 3 = ☐   5 − 1 = ☐

8 − 5 = ☐   6 − 3 = ☐   9 − 4 = ☐

10 − 5 = ☐   7 − 4 = ☐   8 − 3 = ☐

Colour the squares that have an answer of 4.
What can you see?

6 − 1	5 − 1	7 − 2	7 − 4	8 − 2	8 − 3
5 − 2	7 − 3	6 − 3	10 − 1	9 − 7	5 − 4
3 − 2	10 − 6	8 − 5	4 − 4	6 − 4	10 − 5
10 − 7	4 − 0	9 − 6	9 − 5	5 − 0	6 − 5
8 − 3	8 − 4	6 − 2	5 − 1	7 − 3	4 − 4
5 − 3	9 − 4	7 − 1	10 − 6	8 − 6	3 − 0

Note for parent: These activities give practice in
learning the subtraction facts within 10.

Write the missing numbers.

 – 4 = 3   △ – 2 = 4   ● – 3 = 2

8 – = 4   6 – ⬡ = 3   7 – ▢ = 5

▭ – 6 = 3   ⬟ – 5 = 4   10 – ✦ = 6

Draw a line to join each pair of stars with the same answer.

4 – 3

8 – 5

9 – 7

10 – 3

9 – 2

7 – 4

6 – 4

7 – 6

Alphabetical order

Fill in the missing letters and pictures.
You can choose your own pictures to draw.

Note for parent: This activity helps children with alphabetical order and beginning sounds.

m

n

o

p

q

r

s

t

u

v

w

x

y

z

Missing letters a–m

Fill in the missing letters on the snake.

Note for pare... ...ps children to
practise alphabe... ...hout reference.

Super
Star!

Gold Star
Worker!

Searching for words

Read the words in the boxes. Then find them in the big words. Draw a circle around each one you find. The first one has been done for you.

car	too	he	one	ill

or	up	on	she	an

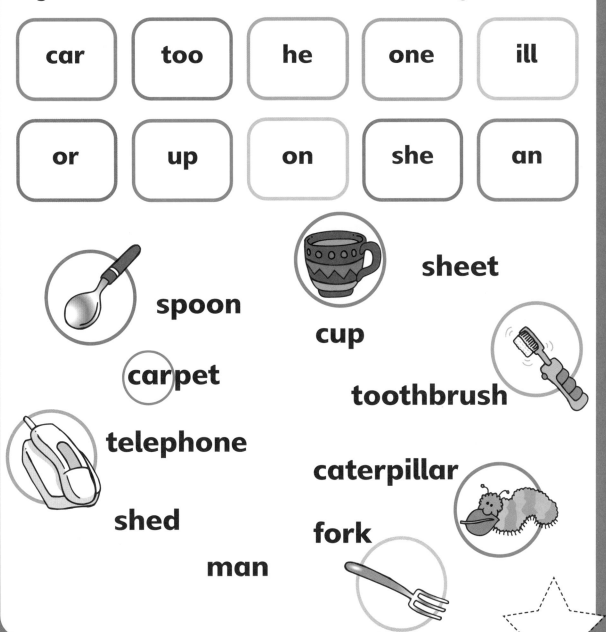

spoon

sheet

cup

carpet

toothbrush

telephone

caterpillar

shed

fork

man

Rhyming pairs

Draw lines to join the pictures that rhyme.

Note to parent: Identifying rhyme
encourages careful listening.

Double beginnings

Choose one of these beginning sounds to complete the words in the boxes.

dr   **fl**   **gr**   **sp**   **cl**

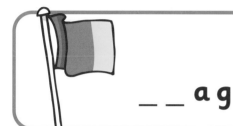 _ _ a g

 _ _ o w n

 _ _ a g o n

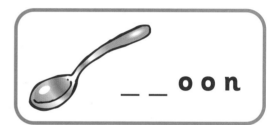 _ _ o o n

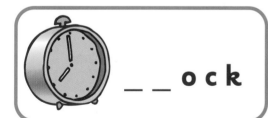 _ _ o c k

 _ _ a p e s

 _ _ o w e r

 _ _ u m

Missing letters n–z

Fill in the missing letters.

Note for parent: This activity helps children to practise alphabetical order without reference.

Finding doubles

Find something in the picture that begins with each of the double sounds on this page. Draw a line to join each double sound to the right object.

tr   **dr**   **ch**   **gl**   **cl**

br   **cr**   **sc**   **fl**   **bl**

Note for parent: This activity helps children to recognize double beginning sounds.

Middle sounds

Draw a circle around the correct middle sounds.

a		o

i		u

o		a

i		e

i		e

a		u

u		a

o		a

i		a

 Note to parent: This activity helps children to choose middle sounds. Some children find this difficult.

Second chance

Fill in the missing letters and pictures. You can choose your own pictures.

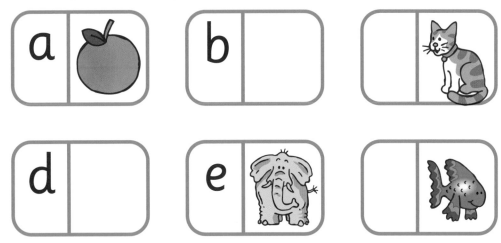

Choose one of these beginning sounds to complete the words in the boxes.

dr   sp   cl

 _ _ a g o n

 _ _ o w n

 _ _ o o n

Note for parent: This page gives a chance to see what children can remember from earlier pages.

Making new words

Write the new words you make.

Change the **b** in **bat**  to make c _ _

Change the **f** in **fox** to make b _ _

Change the **j** in **jar** to make c _ _

Change the **d** in **dog**  to make l _ _

Now draw a picture of each new word in the boxes below. Write the word in the box.

   _ _ _

   _ _ _

_ _ _

   _ _ _

104

 Note to parent: Making these new words gives practice in reading short words.

Little words

Find a little word in each big word. Write the little words in the spaces.

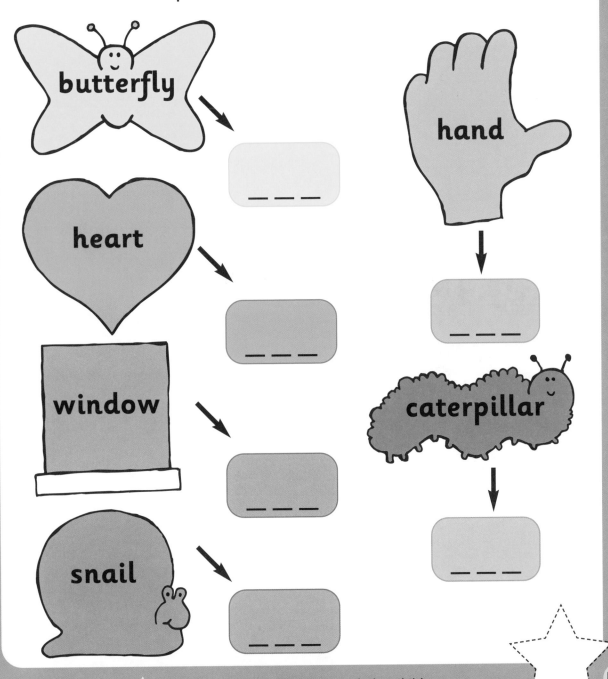

butterfly

_ _ _

heart

_ _ _

window

_ _ _

snail

_ _ _ _

hand

_ _ _

caterpillar

_ _ _

Note to parent: This activity helps children to identify words within words.

Double doubles

Look at the pictures and say the words.
Draw lines to join two pictures that begin in
the same way.

Note to parent: This activity gives further practice
with the double sounds br, sk, dr, gr and cl.

Completing words

Choose one of these double sounds to
complete the words below.

fr sl sp cl tr tw

 _ _ o c k

 _ _ i d e

 _ _ a i n

 _ _ i d e r

 _ _ i n s

 _ _ o g

Note for parent: This activity encourages children to
recognize the double sounds fr, sl, sp, cl, tr and tw.

In the right order

Write the beginning sound of each picture. Then put the three letters in each row into alphabetical order. The first row has been done for you.

Crossword puzzle

Look at the pictures and write the words. The words in the box will help you with your spelling.

globe bread frog flag grapes blue plug

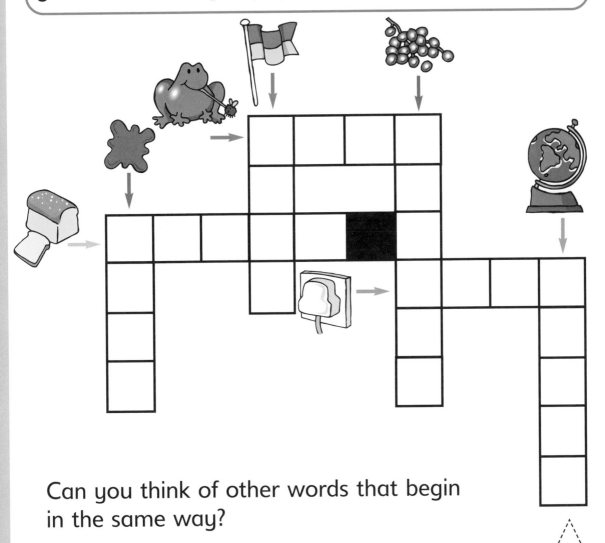

Can you think of other words that begin in the same way?

Note for parent: This activity encourages accurate spelling.

Hidden words

Find a word inside each scarf. Write the words in the spaces. The first one has been done for you.

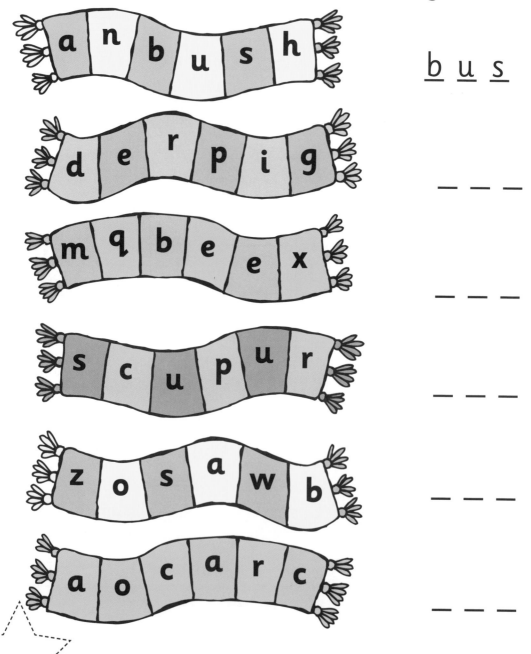

a n b u s h — b u s

d e r p i g — _ _ _

m q b e e x — _ _ _

s c u p u r — _ _ _

z o s a w b — _ _ _

a o c a r c — _ _ _

Note to parent: Searching for words helps with spelling.

Riddles

Read each riddle and write the answer.
You can ask an adult to help you.

The words in the box will help you find the
right answer.

shorts   sheep   shark   shoes   ship   shell

1. This sails across the sea. _ _ _ _

2. You find this on a farm. _ _ _ _ _

3. You wear these on your feet. _ _ _ _ _

4. This fish has very sharp teeth. _ _ _ _ _

5. You find this on the beach. _ _ _ _ _

6. You wear these in the summer. _ _ _ _ _ _

Note for parent: This activity helps with
understanding and spelling.

Last letters

Say the name of each picture.
Tick the correct ending letter.

s	
c	

g	
p	

f	
t	

n	
m	

b	
d	

c	
k	

g	
p	

n	
m	

Note to parent: Children need to listen carefully
to identify last letters.

Matching pairs

Look at the picture. Can you find all the things listed below? Tick each box as you find them.

Find two things that begin with **ch**. ☐ ☐

Find two things that begin with **tr**. ☐ ☐

Find two things that begin with **str**. ☐ ☐

Find two things that begin with **sw**. ☐ ☐

Find two things that begin with **dr**. ☐ ☐

Find two things that begin with **cr**. ☐ ☐

Note for parent: This activity helps children to identify double sounds by both pictures and letters.

Find the animal

Colour in brown all the words beginning with **br**.

Colour in red all the words beginning with **dr**.

Colour in yellow all the words beginning with **st**.

Colour in green all the words beginning with **gl**.

Colour in blue all the words beginning with **sk**.

Colour in purple all the words beginning with **tr**.

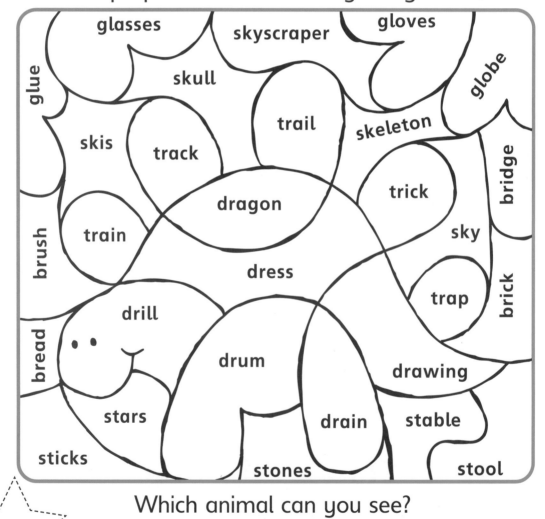

glasses skyscraper gloves

glue skull globe

skis trail skeleton

track bridge

dragon trick

train sky

dress

brush trap

drill brick

bread drum drawing

stars drain stable

sticks stones stool

Which animal can you see?

Note to parent: This activity helps children to identify
the double sounds br, dr, st, gl, sk and tr.

More than one

You add the letter **s** when there is more than one. Write the whole words in the spaces.

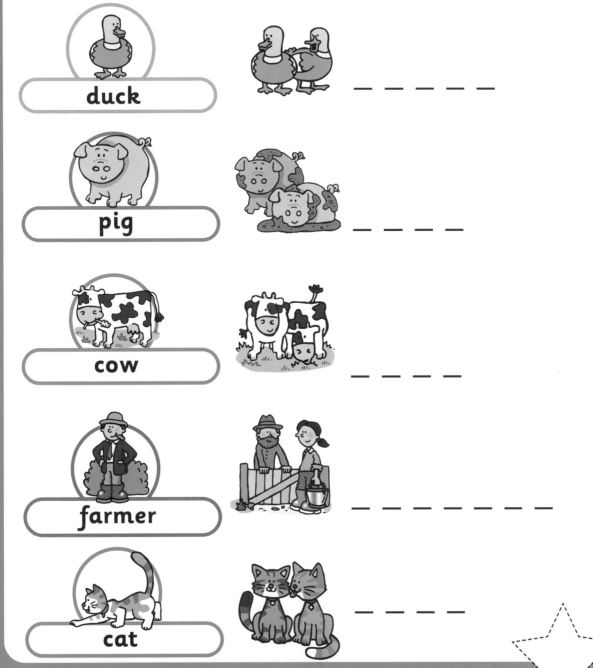

duck _ _ _ _ _

pig _ _ _ _

cow _ _ _ _

farmer _ _ _ _ _ _ _

cat _ _ _ _

 Note for parent: This activity helps children to learn about plurals.

Sorting

Draw each picture in the correct box.

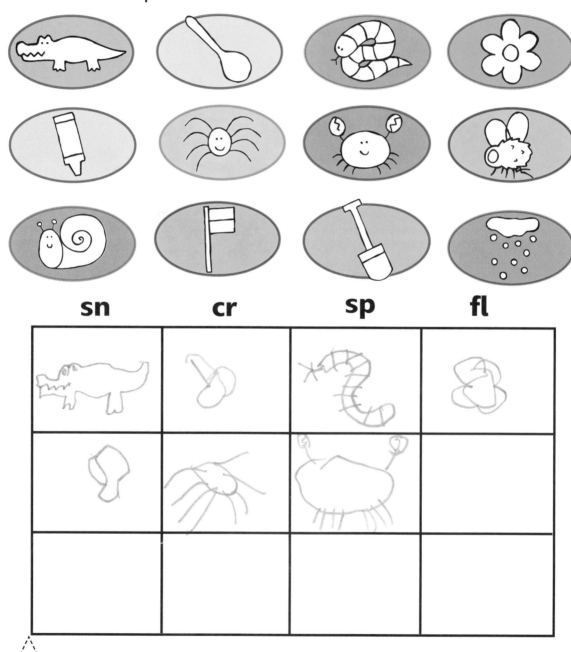

sn	cr	sp	fl

Note to parent: This activity encourages children to classify by beginning sounds.

Second chance

Read each riddle and write the answer. You can ask an adult to help you.

The words in the box will help you find the right answer.

> **sheep   shell   ship**

1. This sails across the sea. _ _ _ _

2. You find this on a farm. _ _ _ _ _

3. You find this on the beach. _ _ _ _ _

Add the letter **s** when there is more than one. Write the whole words in the spaces.

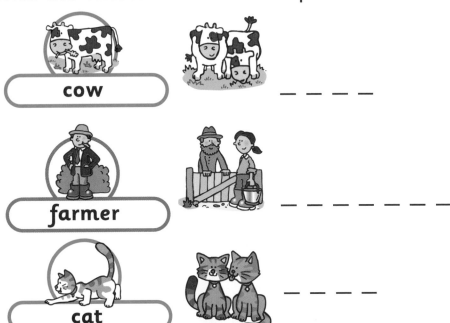

cow

_ _ _ _

farmer

_ _ _ _ _ _ _

cat

_ _ _ _

Note for parent: This page tests what children remember from earlier pages.

Make a word

Draw a line to join two parts together to make a word.

str	ack
tr	asses
gl	erries
bl	ain
ch	ew
scr	ing

Write the words beside the correct pictures.

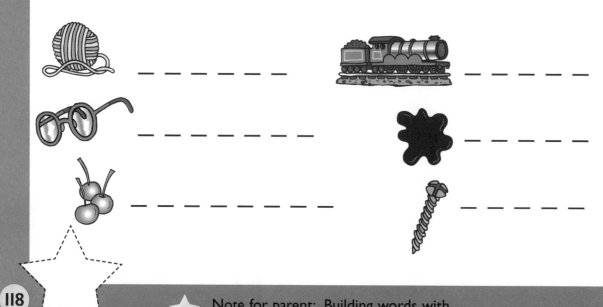

_ _ _ _ _ _ _   _ _ _ _ _ _ _

_ _ _ _ _ _ _   _ _ _ _ _ _ _

_ _ _ _ _ _ _   _ _ _ _ _ _ _

118

Note for parent: Building words with picture clues is an important skill.

Same endings

Join the pictures that end in the same way. Write the last two letters of each word in the spaces. The letters in the box will help you.

ck   sh   ch   ce   ar

_ _   _ _   _ _

_ _   _ _   _ _

_ _   _ _   _ _

   _ _

Note for parent: This activity helps children to listen carefully and to learn about word endings.

Adding the letter e

Add the letter **e** to the end of each word to make a new word. Write the new word and draw a picture of it.

cub _ _ _ _ _

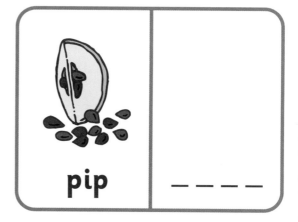

pip _ _ _ _ _

fir _ _ _ _ _

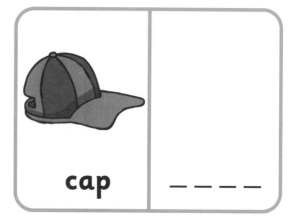

cap _ _ _ _ _

Note for parent: This activity helps children to understand silent 'e'.

Making sets

Some words go together to make sets.
Read the words and write them in the correct set.

car lion bread apple

bus tiger

banana giraffe train

transport

_____

_____

food

_____

_____

_____

animals

_____

_____

_____

Note for parent: This activity encourages children to read words carefully in order to classify them.

Adding to 12

Write the totals.

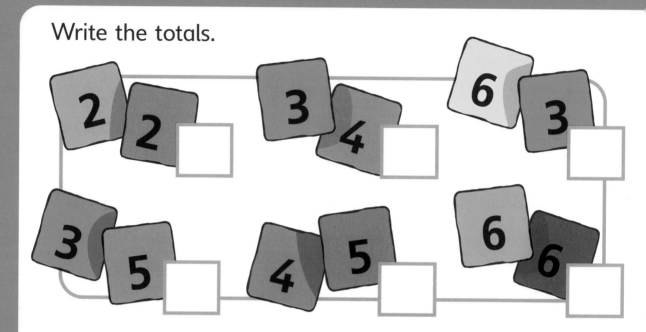

Some pairs of dice have the same total.
Join up the pairs of dice that have the same total.
Which pair of dice is the odd one out?

Note for parent: Encourage your child to work out the totals quickly and not rely on using fingers.

Write the missing number on each boat.

3+5=

2+ ⬜ =10

⬜ +7=12

7+ ⬜ =11

⬜ +5=9

Here is a pair of number adding machines.
Write in the missing numbers.

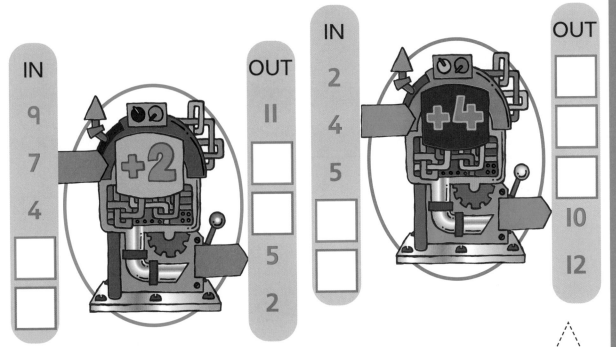

IN

9

7

4

⬜

⬜

OUT

11

⬜

⬜

5

2

IN

2

4

5

⬜

⬜

OUT

⬜

⬜

⬜

10

12

Subtracting to 12

Write the answers at the end of the trail.

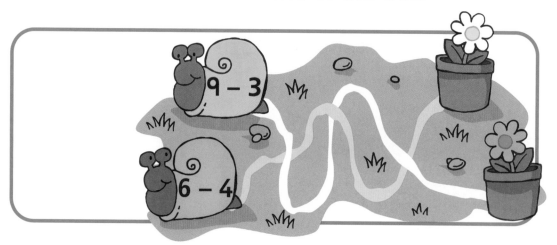

Each child only catches fish to match the number on his or her vest. Join up each child to the correct fish. Colour the fish that no one catches.

Note for parent: Encourage children to work the answers out quickly and not rely on their fingers.

Number mazes

Write the missing numbers.

subtract
3

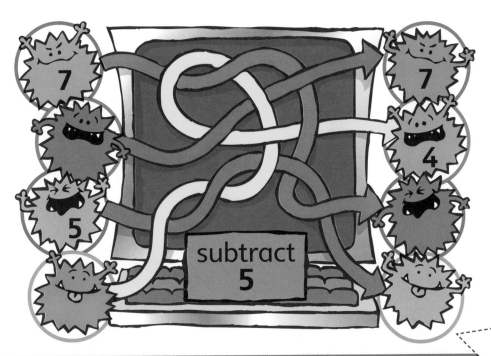

subtract
5

Note for parent: This activity gives further practice in
subtracting up to 12.

Sums up to 12

Whizzy Wendy has made some numbers disappear.
Write in the missing numbers.

$3 + \bigstar = 7$
$\bigstar - 5 = 2$

$4 + \bigstar = 8$
$12 - \bigstar = 6$

$7 + \bigstar = 9$
$\bigstar - 6 = 0$

$6 + \bigstar = 8$
$11 - \bigstar = 8$

Write in the missing sign **+** or **−**.

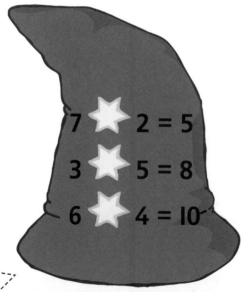

$7 \bigstar 2 = 5$

$3 \bigstar 5 = 8$

$6 \bigstar 4 = 10$

$7 \bigstar 7 = 0$

$5 \bigstar 0 = 5$

$0 \bigstar 6 = 6$

Note for parent: Encourage children to avoid using their fingers to work out these answers.

Join each broomstick to a magic star.
Colour in red the star that has no broomstick.
Colour in blue the star that has two broomsticks.

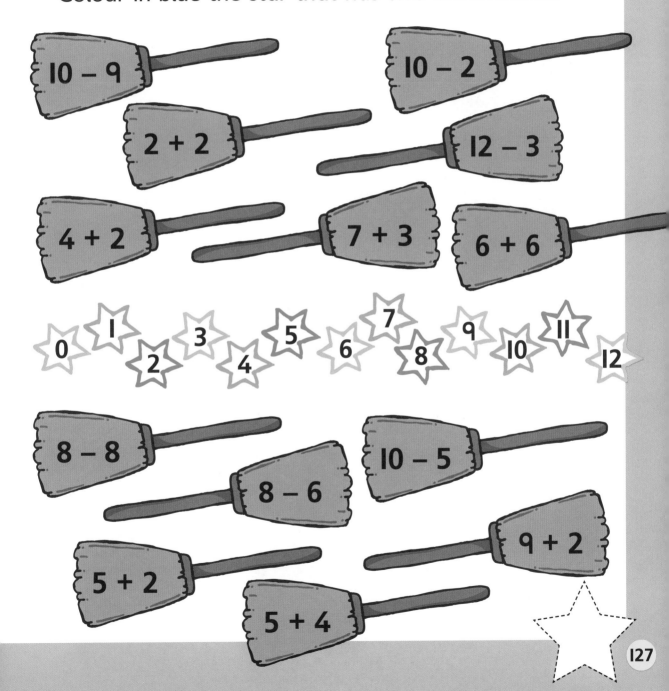

10 – 9

10 – 2

2 + 2

12 – 3

4 + 2

7 + 3

6 + 6

0 1 2 3 4 5 6 7 8 9 10 11 12

8 – 8

10 – 5

8 – 6

5 + 2

9 + 2

5 + 4

Numbers to 100

Join each number to its word.

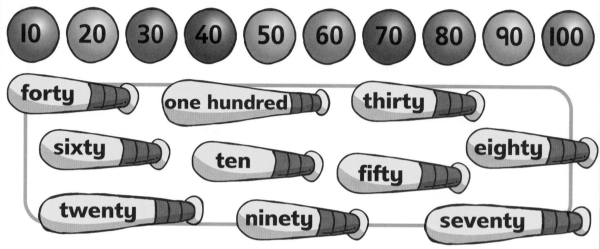

(10) (20) (30) (40) (50) (60) (70) (80) (90) (100)

forty   one hundred   thirty

sixty   ten   eighty

twenty   fifty   ninety   seventy

Write which number comes after each of these.
Colour each even number.

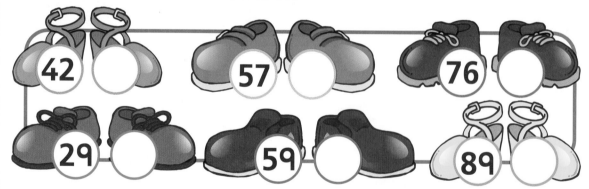

42   57   76

29   59   89

Write which number comes before each of these.
Colour each odd number.

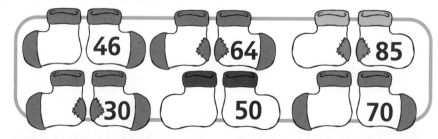

46   64   85

30   50   70

Note for parent: This activity develops ideas of numbers up to 100, including odd and even numbers.

Missing numbers

Write in the missing numbers.

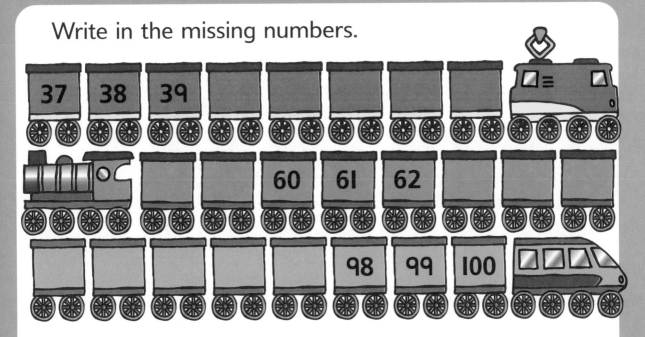

Write in the missing numbers. Colour odd numbers red, and even numbers yellow.

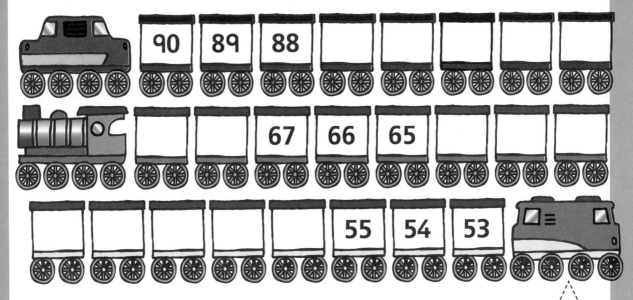

Note for parent: This activity gives further practice with numbers up to 100.

Shapes

Write the missing numbers.

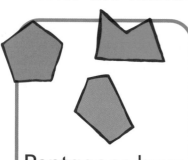 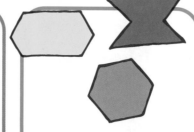 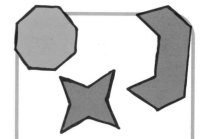

Pentagons have ☐ sides.

Hexagons have ☐ sides.

Octagons have ☐ sides.

Join each shape to its name.

(**triangle**) (**pentagon**) (**hexagon**) (**octagon**)

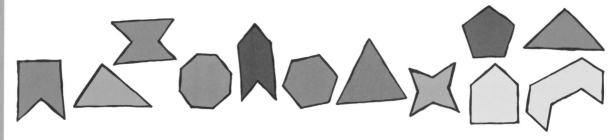

Put a cross on the odd one out in each box.

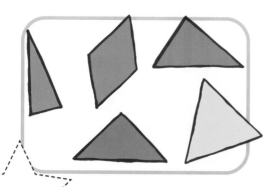 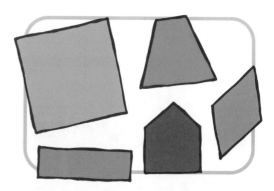

Note for parent: It is useful to know the names of 2-D and 3-D shapes.

These shapes are joined to the correct names.

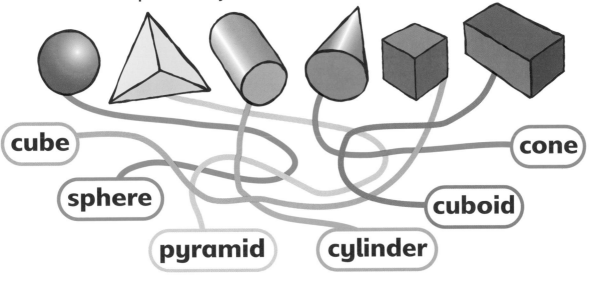

cube

sphere

pyramid

cylinder

cuboid

cone

Join the shapes to their names.

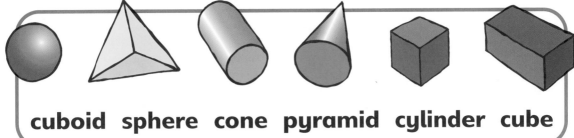

cuboid sphere cone pyramid cylinder cube

Put a cross on the odd one out in each box.

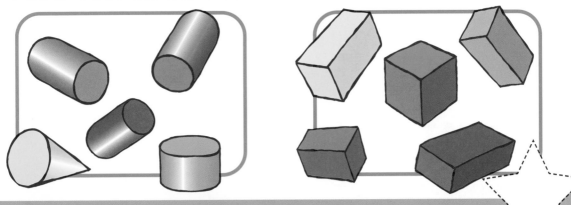

Second chance

Write the missing number in each star.

6 + ⭐ = 9
5 + ⭐ = 10
8 + ⭐ = 11
4 + ⭐ = 12

⭐ + 3 = 6
⭐ + 4 = 8
⭐ + 5 = 11
⭐ + 9 = 12

6 − ⭐ = 0
5 − ⭐ = 1
8 − ⭐ = 8
11 − ⭐ = 3

Colour all the odd numbers.

13 18 24 33 49 65 76 81 85 94

Finish writing the names of the shapes.

t_____   p_____   h_____

 c_____   c_____   p_____

132

Note for parent: This page gives children a chance to see what they can remember.

Adding to 20

The totals on the astronauts match the spaceships. Write in the missing numbers.

Some spaceships have even answers.
Colour them red.

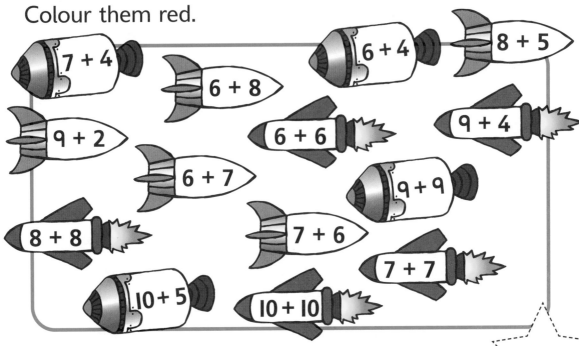

Note for parent: This activity gives more practice in adding numbers up to 20.

Subtracting to 20

Join each mother hen to a chick.

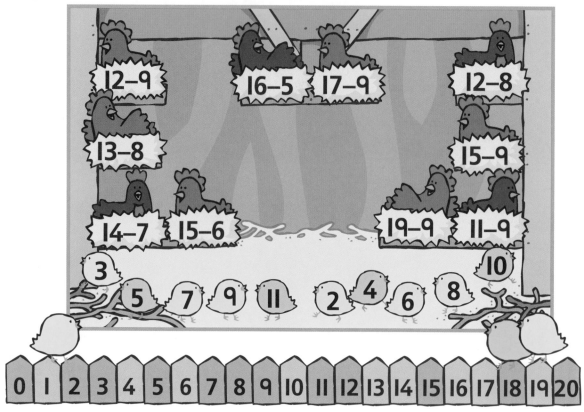

One egg in each basket has a different answer.
Colour the eggs that are the odd ones out.

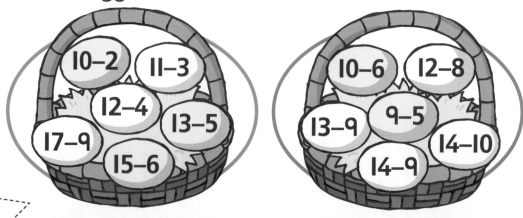

134

Note for parent: If children cannot work out the answers in
their head, encourage them to use the number line.

Write the missing numbers. The answers in each row must match the number on the bucket.

4 | 12 – [ ] | 15 – [ ] | [ ] – 5 | [ ] – 9

6 | 12 – [ ] | 15 – [ ] | [ ] – 5 | [ ] – 9

9 | 12 – [ ] | 15 – [ ] | [ ] – 5 | [ ] – 9

Subtract the smaller number from the larger one to find the difference. Write the answers in the boxes.

16 7   4 13   17 4

20 15   18 12   11 15

Mystery numbers

Write each answer in words. Discover the mystery number in the shaded squares.

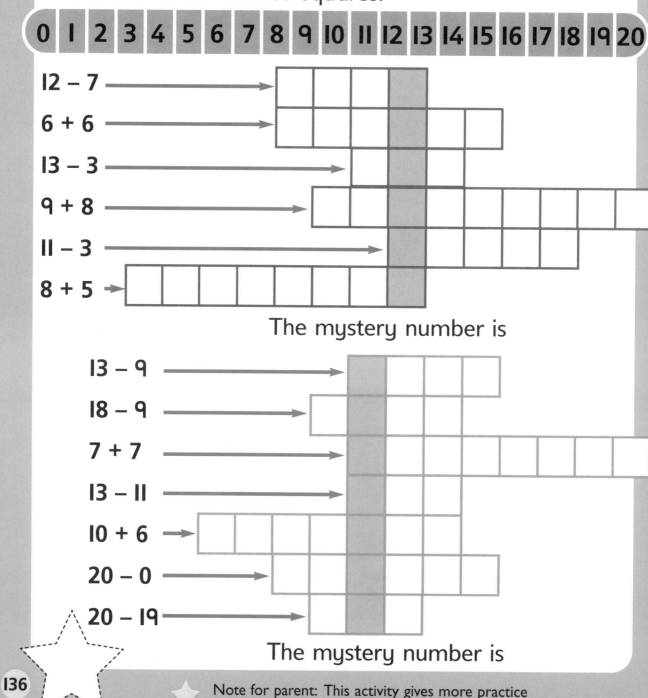

0 1 2 3 4 5 6 7 8 9 10 11 12 13 14 15 16 17 18 19 20

12 − 7

6 + 6

13 − 3

9 + 8

11 − 3

8 + 5

The mystery number is

13 − 9

18 − 9

7 + 7

13 − 11

10 + 6

20 − 0

20 − 19

The mystery number is

Note for parent: This activity gives more practice with addition and with number words.

Odd one out

Work out the answers.
There is an answer in the top fish tank that is not in the bottom one. Colour this fish red.
There is an answer in the bottom fish tank that is not in the top one. Colour this fish yellow.

 Note for parent: Children can use the number line on the facing page to help them work out the answers.

Patterns

Complete the missing half of each picture.

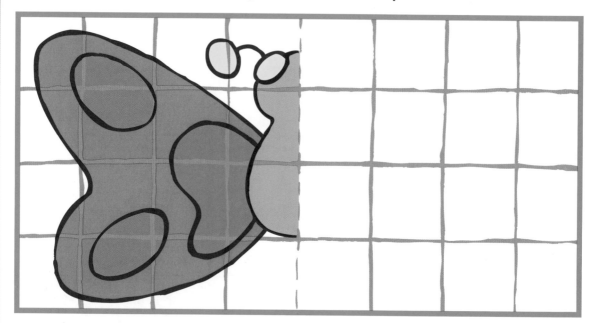

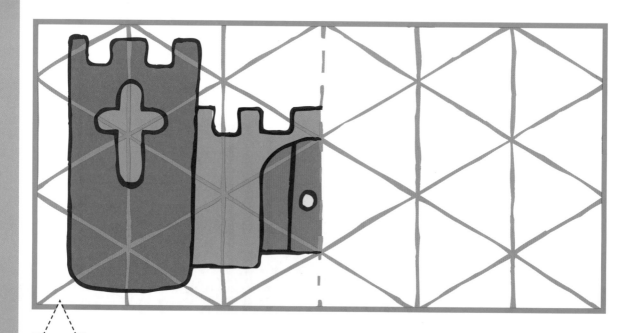

Note for parent: Ideas of pattern and symmetry are important in understanding about shape.

Colour each knight's shield to make a pattern.
Each pattern must be different.

Continue each pattern.

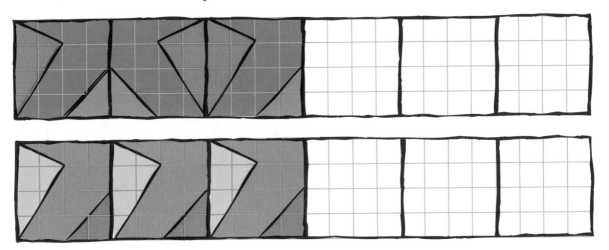

Tens and ones

Write the missing numbers using tens and ones.

15 = 10 + ☐   31 = 30 + ☐   64 = 60 + ☐

16 = 10 + ☐   39 = 30 + ☐   73 = 70 + ☐

19 = 10 + ☐   42 = 40 + ☐   85 = 80 + ☐

12 = ☐ + 2   36 = ☐ + 6   71 = ☐ + 1

25 = ☐ + 5   47 = ☐ + 7   89 = ☐ + 9

28 = ☐ + 8   57 = ☐ + 7   92 = ☐ + 2

13 = ☐ + ☐   43 = ☐ + ☐   62 = ☐ + ☐

26 = ☐ + ☐   48 = ☐ + ☐   75 = ☐ + ☐

Tick the smaller number in each pair.

Note for parent: This shows how large numbers are built up using tens and ones.

Words and numbers

Write the correct number on each child.

Add 1 to each number.

39 · 46 · 73

40

Subtract 1 from each number.

50 · 44 · 68

Add 10 to each number.

34 · 51 · 69

Subtract 10 from each number.

28 · 37 · 52

Note for parent: This activity gives further practice in working with large numbers.

141

Time

Write the missing numbers
on the clock face.

Make the clock
show 7 o'clock.

Make each of these clocks and watches
show 4 o'clock.

Make each of these clocks and watches
show half-past 2.

Note for parent: Telling the time on all kinds of clocks
and watches is important.

One hour passes on each clock. Write the new times.

Join clocks that say the same time.

Draw in the missing minute hand on each clock.

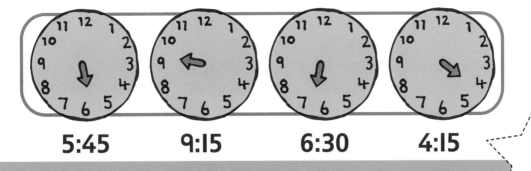

5:45   9:15   6:30   4:15

Second chance

Subtract the smaller number from the larger one to find the difference. Write the answers in the boxes.

| 13 | 17 | 20 | 6 | 12 | 16 |

Colour all the sacks that have EVEN answers.

12 + 8   12 − 6   11 + 6   15 + 3   20 + 15   18 + 12   15 + 11

Write the missing numbers.

twenty-six = 20 + ☐   forty-eight = 40 + ☐

seventy-nine = 70 + ☐   thirty-two = ☐ + 2

sixty-five = ☐ + 5   eighty-four = ☐ + 4

Join the matching answers. Circle the odd one out.

30 + 5   8 + 8   10 + 6

60 + 2   10 + 10   25 + 10   50 + 12

Note for parent: Encourage children to look back if they cannot remember what to do.

Twos and tens

Write the missing numbers in the twos pattern.

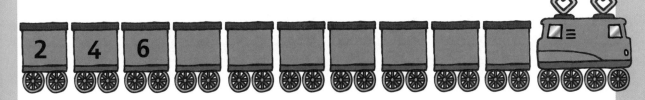

2 | 4 | 6 | | | | | | |

Write the hidden number next to each wheel.

$\bigcirc$ x 2 = 6 $\bigcirc$ x 2 = 10 $\bigcirc$ x 2 = 16

2 x $\bigcirc$ = 20   2 x $\bigcirc$ = 4   2 x $\bigcirc$ = 14

$\bigcirc$ x 2 = 2 $\bigcirc$ x 2 = 18 $\bigcirc$ x 2 = 12

Write the missing numbers in the tens pattern.

10 | 20 | 30 | | | | | | |

Write the hidden number next to each wheel.

$\bigcirc$ x 10 = 30 $\bigcirc$ x 10 = 60 $\bigcirc$ x 10 = 20

10 x $\bigcirc$ = 40   10 x $\bigcirc$ = 90   10 x $\bigcirc$ = 100

$\bigcirc$ x 10 = 80 $\bigcirc$ x 10 = 10

Note for parent: This is an early start to learning multiplication tables.

145

Fives, twos and tens

Write the missing numbers on the fives pattern.

5 10 15

Write the hidden number beside each leaf.

 x 5 = 5

 x 5 = 15

x 5 = 45

5 x 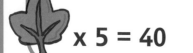 =25

5 x =30

5 x  =10

x 5 = 40

x 5 = 20

x 5 = 35

Write how many fives are in each group.

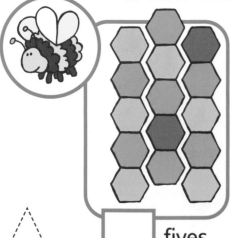

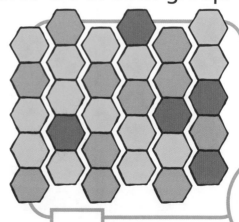

fives

fives

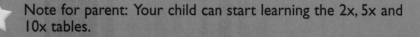

Note for parent: Your child can start learning the 2x, 5x and 10x tables.

Write in the answers to these tables.

2 x 1 = ☐	5 x 1 = ☐	10 x 1 = ☐
2 x 2 = ☐	5 x 2 = ☐	10 x 2 = ☐
2 x 3 = ☐	5 x 3 = ☐	10 x 3 = ☐
2 x 4 = ☐	5 x 4 = ☐	10 x 4 = ☐
2 x 5 = ☐	5 x 5 = ☐	10 x 5 = ☐
2 x 6 = ☐	5 x 6 = ☐	10 x 6 = ☐
2 x 7 = ☐	5 x 7 = ☐	10 x 7 = ☐
2 x 8 = ☐	5 x 8 = ☐	10 x 8 = ☐
2 x 9 = ☐	5 x 9 = ☐	10 x 9 = ☐
2 x 10 = ☐	5 x 10 = ☐	10 x 10 = ☐

Work out the answers. Join each saucer to a cup.

5 x 4

10 x 4

2 x 10

10 x 3

5 x 8

10 x 1

5 x 6

5 x 10

2 x 5

10 x 5

10

20

30

40

50

147

Sharing

Join the balls to the clowns.
Each clown must have the same number of balls.

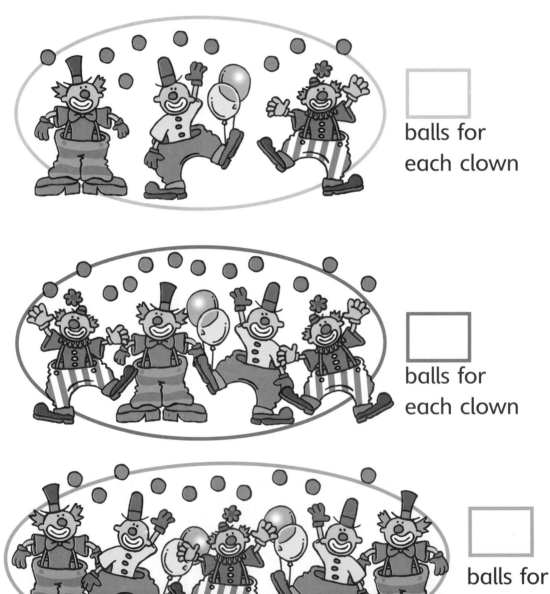

balls for
each clown

balls for
each clown

balls for
each clown

Note for parent: This activity is an introduction to division.

Write how many twos are in each tree.

twos

twos

Write how many threes are on each pond.

threes

threes

Write how many fours are in each bag.

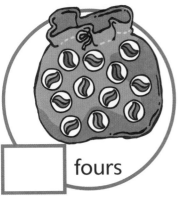

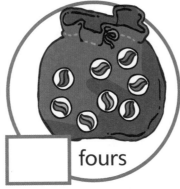

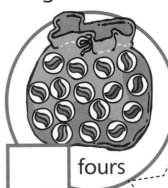

fours

fours

fours

Number words

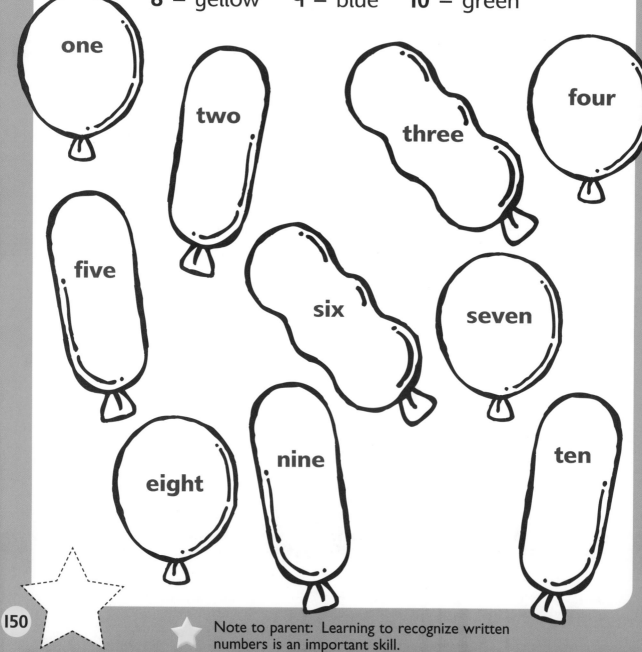

Colour the balloons.

1 = red   2 = purple   3 = yellow   4 = blue
5 = green   6 = red   7 = purple
8 = yellow   9 = blue   10 = green

one

two

three

four

five

six

seven

eight

nine

ten

Note to parent: Learning to recognize written numbers is an important skill.

Word endings

Look at the first picture in each row.
Draw a ring around two pictures in each row that have the same ending as the first.

 Note for parent: This activity encourages children to listen carefully to word endings.

All about nouns

Words that name people, animals, things and places are called nouns. Read these sentences and draw a line under each noun.

The boy is reading a book.

The girl is looking at the television.

The dog is playing with a ball.

The man is cutting the grass.

Find another noun in each picture and write it below.

_____   _____

_____   _____

Note to parent: This activity helps children to learn about nouns.

Adjectives

An adjective tells you more about someone or something.

Choose an adjective to fill in the missing words in the sentences below.

cold   **windy**   **blue**
happy   **small**   **fresh**

1. A ladybird is very _____ .

2. The leaves fell off the tree because it was _____ .

3. The sun was shining and the sky was _____ .

4. Dad had just picked the flowers so they were _____ .

5. The dog was _____ because he had a new ball.

6. It was _____ in the garden and there was ice on the pond.

Note to parent: This activity helps children to understand what an adjective is.

All around you

Look at the picture. Words are missing from some of the signs and labels. Use the words in the box opposite to fill in the spaces.

Note to parent: This activity encourages children to learn about important words in their environment.

Café   Shoe shop   Open   Litter

Main Street   Fish shop   Sale

Bus stop   Post box   Telephone

In the dictionary

A **dictionary** tells you how to spell words.
The words on this page have incorrect spellings.
Look them up in a dictionary and write
them correctly.

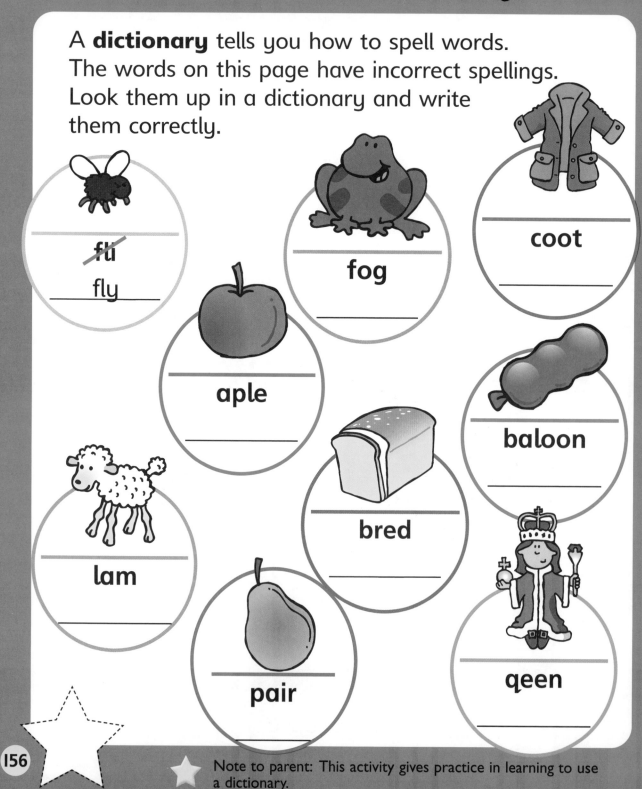

fli
fly

fog

coot

aple

lam

bred

baloon

pair

qeen

156

Dictionary skills

A dictionary also tells you what words mean.
This is called a **definition**. Draw a line to join each
word to the correct definition.

	boy	A creature you read about in fairy tales.
	hutch	A black-and-white bird that cannot fly.
	monster	A tool that has sharp metal teeth.
	saw	A male child.
	penguin	A pet rabbit's home.

Now draw a picture for each word to
make your own picture dictionary.

Note to parent: This activity gives practice in using
definitions.

Using verbs

A **verb** tells you what someone or something is doing. Tick the verb in each box.

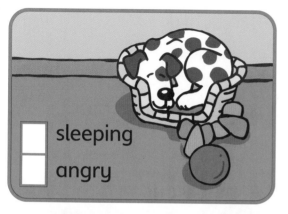

☐	sleeping
☐	angry

☐	happy
☐	licking

☐	running
☐	cold

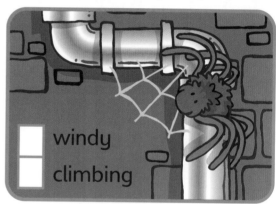

☐	windy
☐	climbing

☐	dirty
☐	swimming

☐	flying
☐	fresh

What are you doing now? _____

Note to parent: This activity helps children to understand verbs.

Second chance

See what you can remember.

Read the words.
Write the number.

two	
six	
three	
eight	
ten	
four	
seven	
nine	
one	
five	

Join each word
ending to a picture.

 ce

 ake

 ing

 er

 ar

 tch

Note to parent: This page gives children a second chance to remember.

Months of the year

Class 2 have made a chart to show when the children have their birthdays.

January	February	March	April
Solomon	Brian	Alison	Imran
Duncan	Jamilla		
May	**June**	**July**	**August**
Ellen	Mark	Dale	Pat
Paul	Lisa	Kerry	Polly
Zara	Ahmed		Frank
Ben			
September	**October**	**November**	**December**
	Meena	Amy	Brendan
	Wendy		Connor
			Sally
			Gail

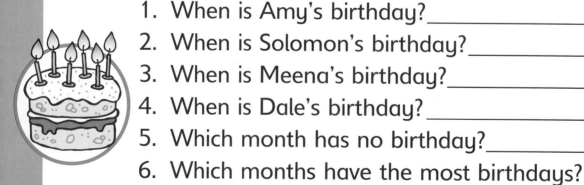

1. When is Amy's birthday?_____
2. When is Solomon's birthday?_____
3. When is Meena's birthday?_____
4. When is Dale's birthday?_____
5. Which month has no birthday?_____
6. Which months have the most birthdays?

_____

When is your birthday?_____

Note to parent: This activity helps children to learn the months of the year.

Fill in the gaps

Use these letters to fill in the gaps: **ai** (nail) or **ea** (meat). Read the words when you have made them.

p_ _ ch

l_ _ f

sn _ _ l

s _ _ l

p _ _ l

s _ _ t

Now use these letters to fill the gaps: **oa** (goat) or **ou** (house).

b _ _ t

m _ _ se

c _ _ t

cl _ _ d

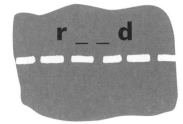

r _ _ d

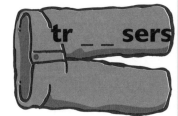

tr _ _ sers

Note to parent: These sounds are not easy. Read the words in brackets to help your child.

Descriptions

Look at the picture. Write a sentence saying what everyone is doing. Try to include a noun, a verb and an adjective in your sentences.

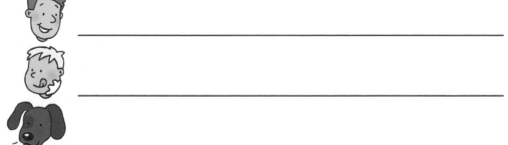

Note to parent: This activity helps children learn how to describe people using proper sentences.

Compound words

You make a compound word by joining two smaller words together.

 **+** **=**

horse   **shoe**   **horseshoe**

Now try to make compound words from the words below:

1 star + fish = _____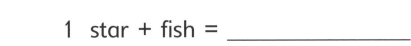

2 water + fall = _____

 3 home + work = _____

4 play + time = _____

 5 tooth + brush = _____

6 foot + ball = _____

 7 ear + ring = _____

 8 book + mark = _____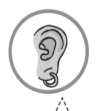

 Note for parent: This activity gives practice in making compound words.

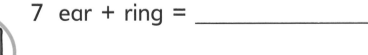

Making new words

You can make new words by changing some of the letters in a word.

change the **p** in **park** to **m** → **mark**
change the **p** in **park** to **sh** → **shark**

Now try to make these new words.

1. Change the **b** in **bear** to **p** → _____

        to **w** → _____

2. Change the **f** in **fire** to **w** → _____

        to **h** → _____

3. Change the **j** in **jaw** to **cl** → _____

        to **str** → _____

4. Change the **br** in **brown** to **cl** → _____

        to **cr** → _____

5. Change the **fl** in **flight** to **br** → _____

        to **kn**→ _____

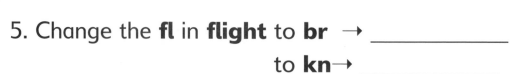
Note for parent: This activity helps children to understand the composition of words.

Reading for meaning

Three children have made a list of what they have in their lunch box. Read the lists and then answer the questions.

Kelly
chicken sandwich
packet of crisps
apple
chocolate cake
can of fizzy drink

Sam
bottle of water
piece of cheese
yoghurt
banana
salad roll

Anna
yoghurt
carton of fruit juice
packet of raisins
cheese sandwich
chocolate biscuit

1. Who has a piece of fruit?_____

2. Who has a yoghurt? _____

3. Who has a sandwich?_____

4. Who has something made of chocolate?

_____

5. Who likes cheese?_____

6. Who has a packet of something?

_____

Make a separate list of what you would like to have in your lunch box.

 Note for parent: This activity gives practice with comprehension and list making.

Speech marks

Read what each animal says.

Write what each animal said using speech marks.
Here is an example: Dog said, "I like to run."

1. Parrot said, "_____."

2. Monkey said, _____.

3. Horse said, _____.

4. Kangaroo said, _____.

5. Elephant said, _____.

Note for parent: This activity gives practice in using speech marks.

Missing letters

Sometimes when we talk to people we do not say every word.

$$I \ am = I'm \qquad It \ is = It's$$

Join the words on the left side of the page to the smaller words on the right.

is not	I'd
cannot	won't
I would	isn't
I am	I'm
will not	you've
you have	can't

Write these sentences again using smaller words instead of the underlined words:

<u>I would</u> like to see you but <u>I am</u> ill. I <u>cannot</u> go out but <u>I would</u> like to see you if you have time and it <u>is</u> <u>not</u> too far for you to come.

_____

_____

_____

_____

Note for parent: Try to explain how an apostrophe is always used in these shortened versions.

Writing postcards

Write a postcard to a relative (for example your granny, a cousin, an uncle) telling them about your school.

Dear _____

Draw a picture that might be on the other side of the postcard, or cut out a picture and stick it here.

 Note for parent: Postcard writing is good practice.

Speech bubbles

Look at what is happening in each picture.
What do you think the people are saying?
Write the words in the speech bubbles.

 Note for parent: This activity gives practice in interpreting picture stories.

169

Reading instructions

Read the instructions and then draw on the pictures.

1. Draw a hat on the first clown.

2. Draw long shoes on the second clown.

3. Draw spots on the trousers of the third clown.

4. Draw a flower on the hat of the second clown.

5. Draw curly hair on the third clown.

6. Draw a smile on the face of the first clown.

7. Draw a bow-tie on the first clown and the third clown.

8. Draw buttons on the shirts of the second clown and the third clown.

Note for parent: This activity gives practice in following instructions.

Silly or sensible?

Some of these sentences are silly, and some are sensible. Read each one and then write the word **silly** or **sensible** beside it.

1. A library is a place to borrow babies. _____

2. Clocks help us to tell the time. _____

3. All boys have black hair. _____

4. Teachers like to teach bananas. _____

5. Cats have baby puppies. _____

6. There are lots of animals at the zoo. _____

Now write two sentences yourself:

A silly sentence: _____

_____

A sensible sentence: _____

_____

 Note for parent: In this activity children can practise responding to different sentences.

Odd one out

Cross out the word that does not belong in each row.

1 **Monday**   May   Friday   Tuesday   Sunday
2 square   triangle   circle   shape   rectangle
3 paint   red   orange   blue   green
4 sheep   horse   pig   cow   lion
5 bus   car   man   lorry   van

Now put the words in the correct group.

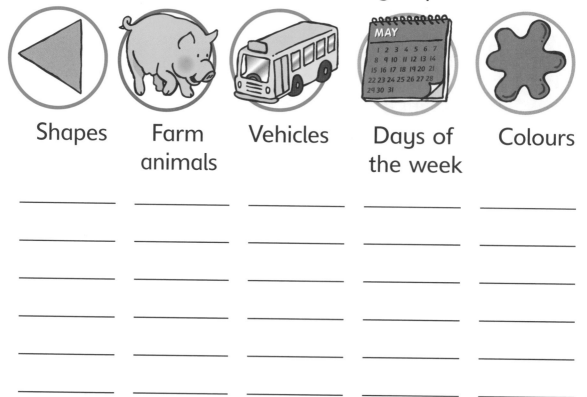

Shapes   Farm   Vehicles   Days of   Colours
          animals   the week

Can you add two words of your own to each list?

 Note for parent: This activity helps children to understand
categories of words.

Second chance

See what you can remember.

Make these words shorter.

is not   I would   cannot

_____   _____   _____

Sort these words into the three boxes below.

> dog   tall   grows   soft   mouse
> run   tree   cold   squeaks

nouns

verbs

adjectives

Note for parent: This page gives children a second
chance to remember.

173

Opposites

An antonym is a word that has the opposite meaning to another word.

big   **small**   **happy**   **sad**

Read the words in the box.

pull	near	dry	cold	full
hard	long	light	last	day

Use the words in the box to write the antonym of each word in this list.

1. wet _____

2. soft _____

3. first _____

4. far _____

5. empty _____

6. hot _____

7. night _____

8. push _____

9. short _____

10. heavy _____

Note for parent: This activity helps children to understand and use opposites.

Finish the sentences

Draw a line to join the beginning of each sentence to the correct ending.

1. The dog barked   into the air.

2. The horse galloped   a big web.

3. The frog jumped   on the wall.

4. The birds flew   at the burglar.

5. The spider spun   across the field.

6. The cat slept   out of the pond.

Now finish these sentences.

The dolphin jumped _____.

The kangaroo hopped _____.

Note for parent: This activity helps with comprehension and making choices.

175

Word search

Look for these words in the grid below.

nouns	verbs	adjectives
dog	runs	fast
tree	grows	tall
mouse	squeaks	soft

a	e	m	c	i	g	r	t	h	j
s	r	l	c	b	t	a	l	q	k
d	o	g	s	g	r	o	w	s	z
f	k	f	m	u	e	s	b	g	s
d	g	s	t	t	e	q	n	q	u
r	u	n	s	u	f	u	d	m	p
p	x	a	l	j	y	e	u	o	n
w	f	l	o	o	v	a	l	u	t
y	a	z	e	v	n	k	y	s	b
t	h	x	a	e	c	s	w	e	d

Now find all the letters of the alphabet and colour them red. There are 26 to find.

Note for parent: This activity helps children to recognize nouns, verbs and adjectives.

A puzzle page

Make as many words as you can from the letters.

p	o	r
l	e	t
i	s	a
r	e	m

You can move in any direction but do not jump a square.

_____   _____

_____   _____

_____   _____

_____   _____

How many words did you find?

Change one letter to make a new word.

man   _____   You cook food in this.

coat   _____   You go on water in this.

robber_____   You rub out with this.

card   _____   A horse can pull this.

fork   _____   Soldiers live in this.

wolf   _____   This is a sport.

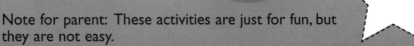

Making totals

Count each set. Write the totals.

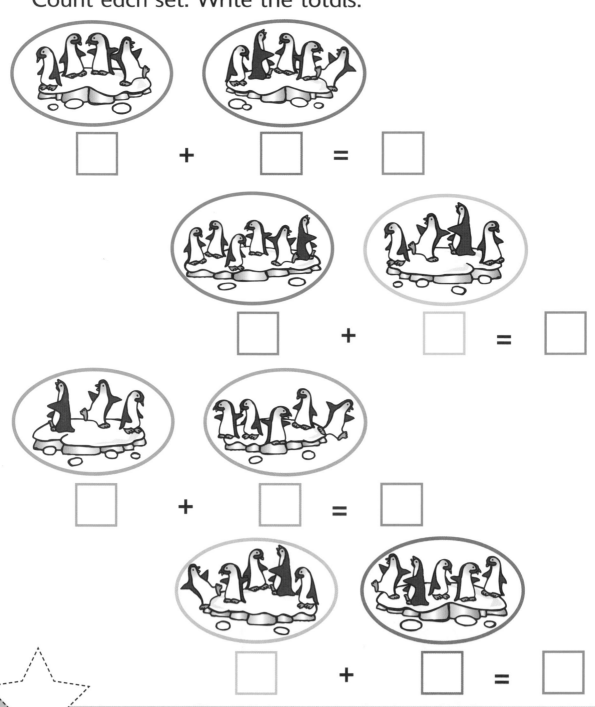

☐ + ☐ = ☐

☐ + ☐ = ☐

☐ + ☐ = ☐

☐ + ☐ = ☐

Note for parent: This activity gives your child practice in combining sets to make totals.

Draw snowflakes to make the totals.

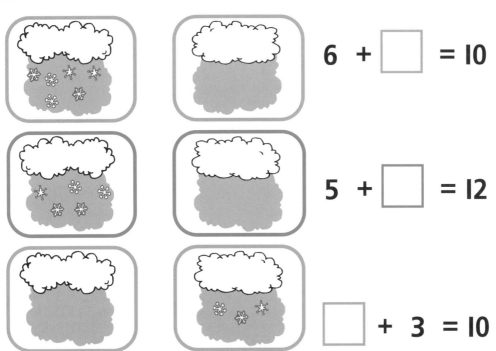

$6 + \boxed{} = 10$

$5 + \boxed{} = 12$

$\boxed{} + 3 = 10$

Join pairs of numbers that total 12.

4
3
7
9
6
5
6
8

Taking away

Cross out four items on each shelf.
Write how many are left.

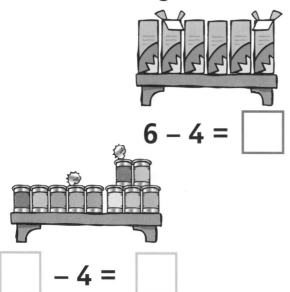

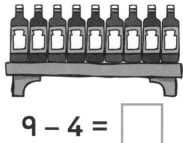

9 – 4 = ☐

6 – 4 = ☐

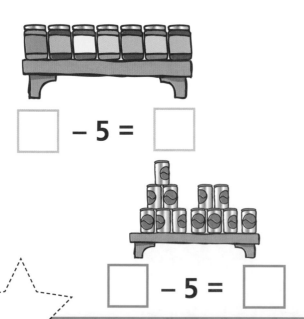

☐ – 4 = ☐

☐ – 4 = ☐

Cross out five in each set. Write how many are left.

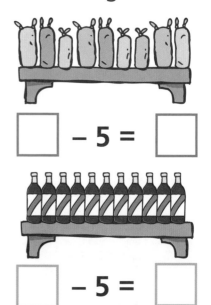

☐ – 5 = ☐

☐ – 5 = ☐

☐ – 5 = ☐

☐ – 5 = ☐

Note for parent: This activity gives your child practice in subtraction by taking amounts away.

Coco the clown has 12 balloons. Write the new totals in the boxes.

Sam buys
3 balloons.

12 – 3 = ☐

Coco loses
1 balloon.

9 – 1 = ☐

Lucy buys
5 balloons.

8 – 5 = ☐

Coco gives
2 balloons away.

3 – 2 = ☐

Counting on

Use the number line to count on. Show the jumps and write the answers. The first one has been done for you.

$12 + 3 = \boxed{15}$

10 11 12 13 14 15 16 17 18 19

$8 + 4 = \boxed{}$

6 7 8 9 10 11 12 13 14 15

$7 + 7 = \boxed{}$

7 8 9 10 11 12 13 14 15 16

$9 + 6 = \boxed{}$

8 9 10 11 12 13 14 15 16 17

$11 + 5 = \boxed{}$

9 10 11 12 13 14 15 16 17 18

Note for parent: A number line or track is useful for counting on to help add numbers.

Counting back

Show the jumps and write the answers.

14 − 5 = ☐

6 7 8 9 10 11 12 13 14 15 16 17

18 − 6 = ☐

9 10 11 12 13 14 15 16 17 18 19 20

16 − 7 = ☐

7 8 9 10 11 12 13 14 15 16 17 18

Use the number track to count back
and answer these.

1 2 3 4 5 6 7 8 9 10 11 12 13 14 15 16 17 18 19 20

10 − 4 = ☐   13 − 5 = ☐   11 − 3 = ☐

14 − 6 = ☐   12 − 4 = ☐   15 − 6 = ☐

17 − 4 = ☐   16 − 3 = ☐

Note for parent: Use the number track to help
take one number from another by counting back.

Machines

Total the numbers going into the machines.

Write the numbers coming out of this machine.

Note for parent: Ask your child to look at the numbers going into each machine and work out the numbers coming out.

Write the numbers coming out of these machines.

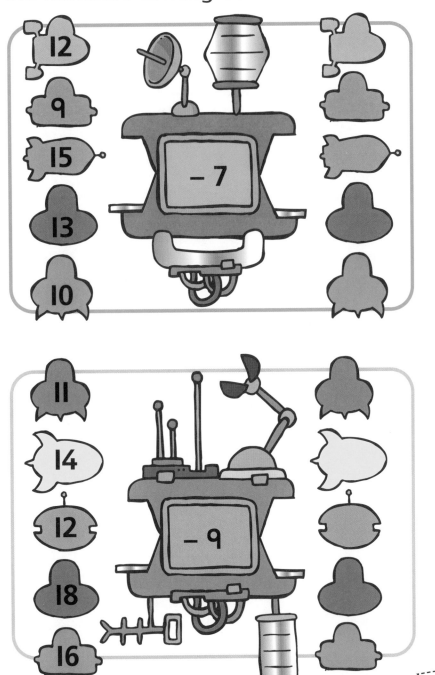

Differences

The difference between 4 and 9 is 5.
Write the differences between the numbers below.

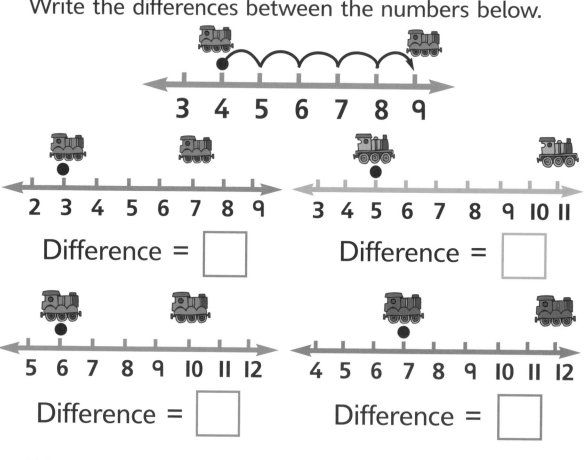

3 4 5 6 7 8 9

2 3 4 5 6 7 8 9

Difference = ☐

3 4 5 6 7 8 9 10 11

Difference = ☐

5 6 7 8 9 10 11 12

Difference = ☐

4 5 6 7 8 9 10 11 12

Difference = ☐

What is the difference between these pairs
of numbers?

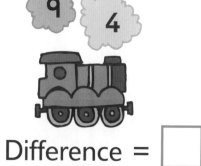

9   4

Difference = ☐

6   11

Difference = ☐

186

Find the pairs of numbers with a difference of 6.
Colour each matching pair.

Fill in the missing number so that each boat has a
difference of 5. The first one has been done for you.

Addition bonds

Make these totals in different ways. The first one has been done for you.

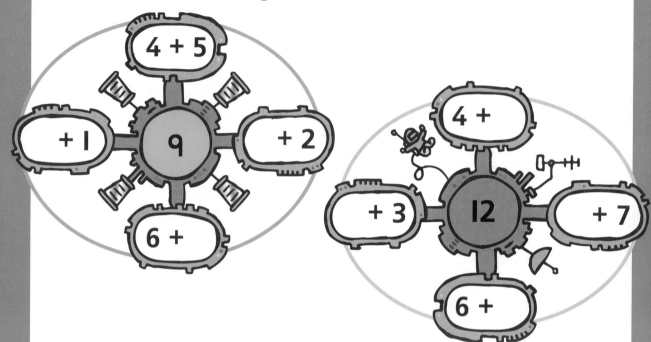

Write your own numbers for this spacestation.

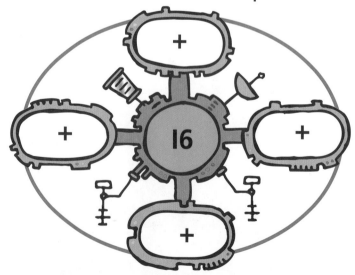

Note for parent: Addition bonds are all the different ways that a total can be made with two numbers.

Second chance

Count each set. Write the total.

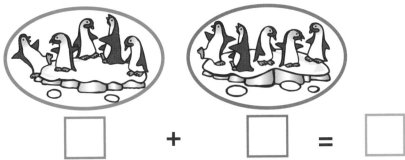

☐ + ☐ = ☐

Cross out four items on each shelf. Write how many are left.

 6 – 4 = ☐

 ☐ – 4 = ☐

Write the numbers coming out of this machine.

11

14

12

– 9

18

16

Adding to 20

Answer each of these sums. Use the code to find the names of the four mystery vegetables.

$12+4=$ | 16 | p

$9+9=$ [ ] _

$6+5=$ [ ] _

$7+5=$ [ ] _

$2+9=$ [ ] _

$10+7=$ [ ] _

$8+9=$ [ ] _

$9+6=$ [ ] _

$10+9=$ [ ] _

11	a
12	c
13	i
14	n
15	o
16	p
17	r
18	e
19	t
20	b

$12+8=$ [ ] _

$11+7=$ [ ] _

$8+3=$ [ ] _

$7+7=$ [ ] _

$8+8=$ [ ] _

$11+4=$ [ ] _

$12+7=$ [ ] _

$6+5=$ [ ] _

$5+14=$ [ ] _

$8+7=$ [ ] _

Note for parent: Ask your child how he or she worked out each answer. Children will answer some of the facts quickly.

Fill in the missing numbers to complete these addition walls. The first one has been done for you.

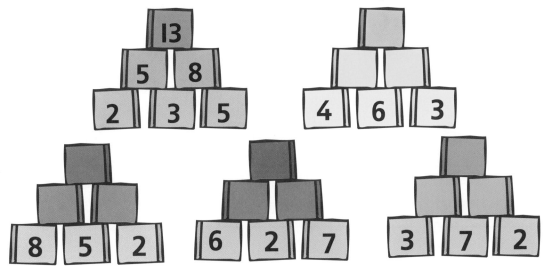

Write the numbers to complete these adding chains. The first answer has been done for you.

3 | +2 | 5 | +5 | | +3 | | +7 |

1 | +3 | | +6 | | +2 | | +8 |

2 | +5 | | +1 | | +6 | | +6 |

Subtraction bonds

Find the different ways of making 5.

12 – ☐

9 – ☐

5

☐ – 8

☐ – 6

Find the different ways of making 6.

☐ – 4

11 – ☐

6

9 – ☐

14 – ☐

Join the shells to the correct crabs.

15 – 8   17 – 9   14 – 6   13 – 9   11 – 4   12 – 8

4   7   8

Note for parent: Show your child that answers to subtractions can be made in different ways.

Circle the odd one out in each set.

Join the matching answers.

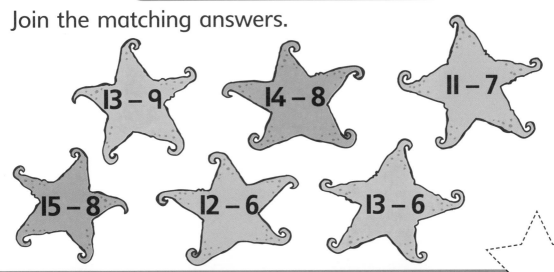

Take away facts

Write the answers to these in words. Find the
mystery number in the shaded squares.

14 – 7 ⟶

11 – 6 ⟶

13 – 7 ⟶

17 – 5 ⟶

13 – 5 ⟶

16 – 15 ⟶

16 – 7 ⟶

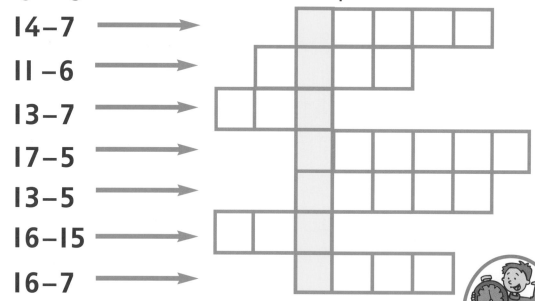

Answer these as quickly as you can.
Time yourself and try to beat your best time.

9 – 4 = ☐   12 – 6 = ☐   8 – 4 = ☐

8 – 7 = ☐   7 – 4 = ☐   13 – 8 = ☐

11 – 6 = ☐   15 – 10 = ☐   6 – 2 = ☐

7 – 5 = ☐   9 – 6 = ☐   10 – 5 = ☐

10 – 7 = ☐   11 – 4 = ☐   14 – 7 = ☐

Note for parent: These activities give practice in learning the subtraction facts within 20.

Fill in the missing numbers to make each total.
The first one has been done for you.

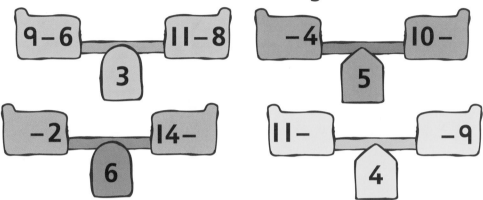

9–6   11–8
   3

–4   10–
   5

–2   14–
   6

11–   –9
   4

Write in your own numbers to make the total.

–   –
   7

Complete the number trails back to zero.

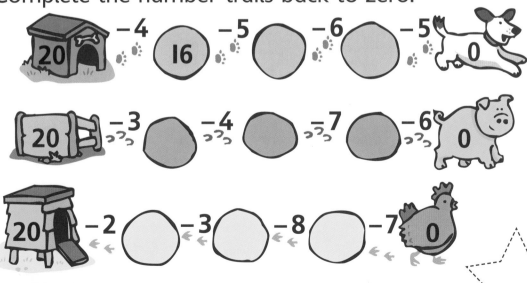

20 –4 16 –5 ◯ –6 ◯ –5 0

20 –3 ◯ –4 ◯ –7 ◯ –6 0

20 –2 ◯ –3 ◯ –8 ◯ –7 0

Add three numbers

Find the total of the three numbers.
Write the total in the centre.

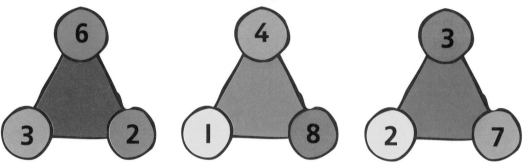

Write the missing numbers.

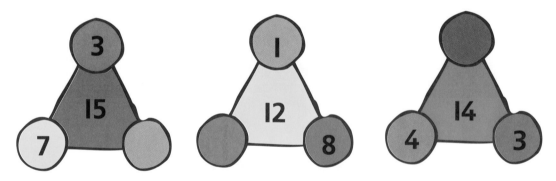

Write a number in each shape. Make each triangle equal 20. The first one has been done for you.

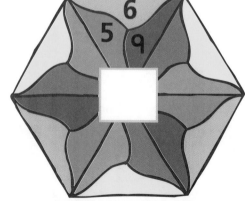

Note for parent: When adding three numbers, look for pairs of numbers that are easy to add and then add on the third number.

Money totals

How much money is in each purse? Write the answers in the boxes.

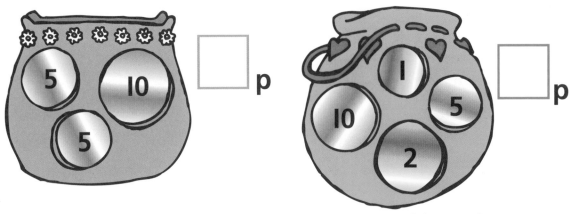

☐ p

☐ p

What is the total cost of each group of items? Write the answers in the boxes.

£3 £4 £6 £7 £5

£ ☐

£ ☐

£ ☐

Note for parent: This activity gives practice in totalling coins and exact pounds.

Doubles

Answer these doubles as quickly as you can.

4 + 4 = ☐   6 + 6 = ☐   3 + 3 = ☐

5 + 5 = ☐   8 + 8 = ☐   2 + 2 = ☐

7 + 7 = ☐   10 + 10 = ☐   9 + 9 = ☐

Use the doubles above to help answer these.
Join the sums to the correct answers.

3 + 4

10 + 9

5 + 6

5 + 4

6 + 7

8 + 9

8 + 7

7
9
11
13
15
17
19

Note for parent: If children know doubles, they can use this to work out 'near doubles', e.g. 6 + 6 is 12, so 6 + 7 is one more.

Giving change

Draw coins to show the change from 20p.
Write the amount of change.

7p [   ] [   ] p

8p [   ] [   ] p

12p [   ] [   ] p

15p [   ] [   ] p

Write the change from 20p for each of these.

11p   change: [   ] p

14p   change: [   ] p

6p   change: [   ] p

9p   change: [   ] p

16p   change: [   ] p

Hidden numbers

Leaves have hidden some of the numbers on the snakes. Write the missing numbers.

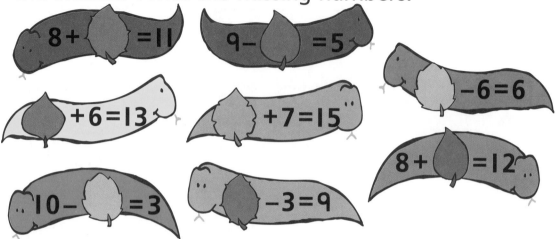

$8+=11$

$9-=5$

$-6=6$

$+6=13$

$+7=15$

$8+=12$

$10-=3$

$-3=9$

Work out the answers. Colour the even numbers red. Colour the odd numbers blue. Which number is hidden in the picture?

7−6	3+4	4+3		9−4	
			7+7	11−5	14−9
11+6	7−5	2+1	8−2	8−7	
			6+6		10+3
	1+8	4+6	5+6	9−3	10−6	3+4
					11+7	7+6
13−6	9−7	6+3	8+7	9−4	4+4
				3+6		8−3
12−5	8+4	9+4	9+9	11−7	
6−1		4+9	3+2	12−3

Note for parent: This activity gives practice in adding and taking away numbers to 20.

Second chance

Write the numbers to complete these adding chains.

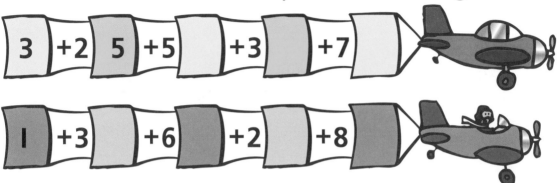

3 +2 5 +5 ⬜ +3 ⬜ +7 ⬜

1 +3 ⬜ +6 ⬜ +2 ⬜ +8 ⬜

Circle the odd one out in each set.

11 − 5   12 − 6

15 − 9   17 − 9

13 − 6
18 − 9
15 − 8
14 − 7

Write the change from 20p for each of these.

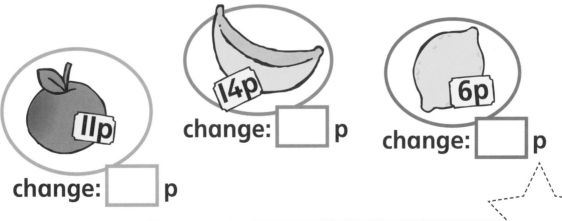

11p

change: ⬜ p

14p

change: ⬜ p

6p

change: ⬜ p

Note for parent: This page is another chance to find out what your child can remember.

Large numbers

Write the missing numbers in these patterns.

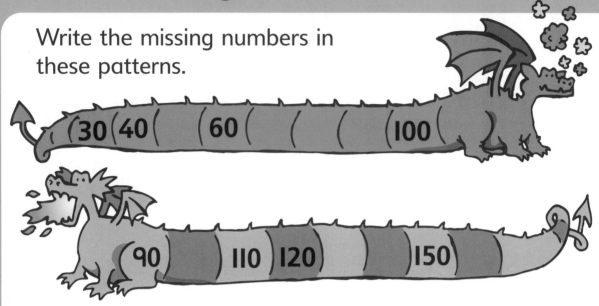

30 40 [ ] 60 [ ] [ ] 100 [ ]

90 [ ] 110 120 [ ] 150

Write the totals in the boxes. Use the first answer to help you work out the second answer.

7+2= ☐
70+20= ☐

4+3= ☐
40+30= ☐

3+5= ☐
30+50= ☐

6+5= ☐
60+50= ☐

Note for parent: Look at the pattern between the addition facts and the multiples of 10.

Draw a line to match each dragon to the correct cave.

90+60=

120

110

70+70=

50+80=

90

150

50+70=

140

60+30=

130

70+40=

Word endings

Look at the first picture in each row. Draw a ring around another picture in the row that has the same ending.

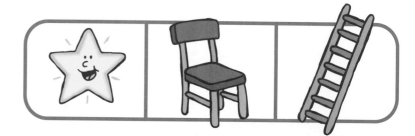

Note for parent: This activity helps children to recognize the endings ll, ck, ing and er.

Read the sentences and write your answers in the spaces. The pictures will help you.

You get water from this.

_ _ l l

You put your key into this.

_ _ c k

He wears a crown on his head.

_ _ n g

You put this in a post box.

_ _ _ _ e r

Learning about **ar**

Complete each word with the letters **ar**.
Draw a picture in each box.

 c a r

 s t _ _

 s c _ _ f

 b _ _ n

 s h _ _ k

 c _ _ d

 Note for parent: This activity helps children to practise the sound ar, and to read words.

Long vowels

Add an **e** to the end of each word and see how the middle sound changes. It's a magic **e**! Then draw the pictures.

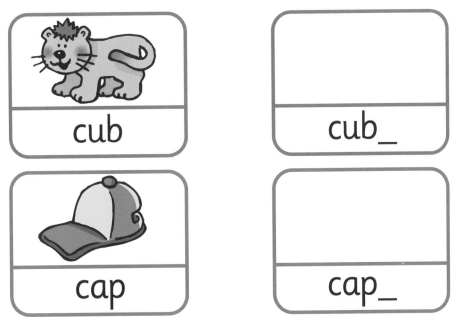

cub

cub_

cap

cap_

Can you think of a word that rhymes with each of the words below? Write your answers in the spaces.

mice _ _ _ _

cake _ _ _ _

nose _ _ _ _

tube _ _ _ _

Note to parent: This activity helps children to learn about long vowel sounds.

Finding words

Draw a ring around the words you can make from the letters in the word **elephant**.

elephant

hat	put	tea	ant
pot	was	help	let
one	leap	net	had

Now make as many words as you can from the letters in the word **aeroplane**.

I made words.

Note to parent: This activity helps children to spell simple words.

Word grid

Find the names of five animals. Find the names of five insects. The pictures will help you. Remember to look across and down.

f	a	q	c	a	t
l	n	d	o	s	l
y	t	o	w	h	s
p	i	g	b	e	e
w	o	r	m	n	p
s	n	a	i	l	y

 Note for parent: This activity helps children with spelling.

Alphabetical order

Look at the pictures. Write the correct word underneath each one. Then write the words in alphabetical order in the box.

a b c d e f g h i j k l m
n o p q r s t u v w x y z

– – –   – – –   – – –   – – –

1	
2	
3	
4	
5	
6	
7	
8	

– – –   – – –

Note for parent: This activity helps children become more familiar with alphabetical order.

Choose a middle

Choose **oo** or **ee** to finish the words below.

 h_ _k

 c_ _k

 t_ _th

 b_ _k

 ch_ _se

 tr_ _

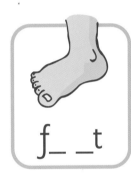 f_ _t

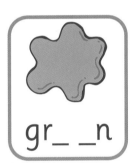 gr_ _n

Fill in the spaces to complete these riddles.

You see this in the sky at night.   _ o o _

You have two of these to walk on. _ e e _

More middle sounds

Choose **ai** or **oa** to finish the words below.

n_ _l

b_ _t

c_ _t

g_ _t

s_ _l

t_ _l

sn_ _l

ch_ _n

s_ _p

Fill in the spaces to complete these riddles.

You get wet if this falls on you. _ a i _

You might eat this for breakfast. _ o a _ _

Note to parent: This activity encourages children to listen carefully.

Rhyming picture

Look at the picture. Then write the answers to the questions.

1. What rhymes with **tall**? _ _ _ _

2. What rhymes with **bees**? _ _ _ _ _ _

3. What rhymes with **log**? _ _ _ _

4. What rhymes with **string**? _ _ _ _ _ _

5. What rhymes with **skate**? _ _ _ _

5. What rhymes with **bite**? _ _ _ _

 Note for parent: This activity gives practice with double and treble sounds at the end of words.

Riddles

Write the answer that rhymes. Draw a picture in each box. Make up your own rhyme for the last box using **ou** in the middle.

You use this to eat ice cream. It rhymes with **moon**.	_ _ _ _ _
This is a green vegetable. It rhymes with **tea**.	_ _ _
This animal moves very slowly. It rhymes with **tail**.	_ _ _ _ _
You wear this outdoors. It rhymes with **boat**.	_ _ _ _

Note to parent: This activity involves simple reading and recognition of rhyme.

Second chance

Look at the first picture in each row.
Draw a ring around another picture that has the same ending.

Choose **oo** or **ee** to finish the words below.

h_ _k   c_ _k   t_ _th

Note to parent: This activity is a chance to see what children have remembered.

Endings

Read the word in each row. Draw a circle around two pictures that end in the same way.

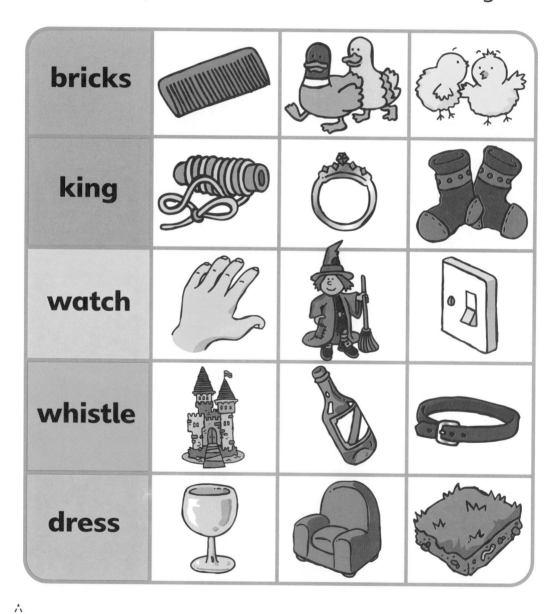

bricks	comb	ducks	chicks
king	rope	ring	boots
watch	hand	witch	switch
whistle	castle	bottle	belt
dress	glass	chair	rug

Note to parent: This activity encourages children to listen carefully to the ends of words.

Making pairs

Draw a line to join two pictures that begin in the same way. Write the beginning sound under each picture.

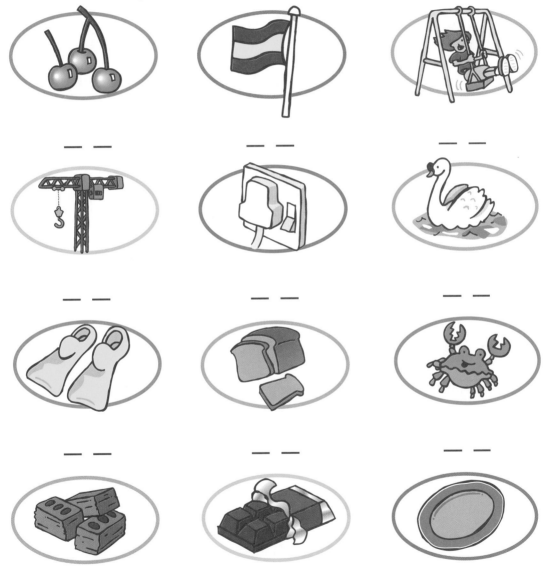

Note for parent: This activity gives children practice with the beginning sounds br, ch, cr, fl, pl and sw.

Short vowels

Write in the missing letter **a**, **e**, **i**, **o** or **u**.
These letters are called vowels.

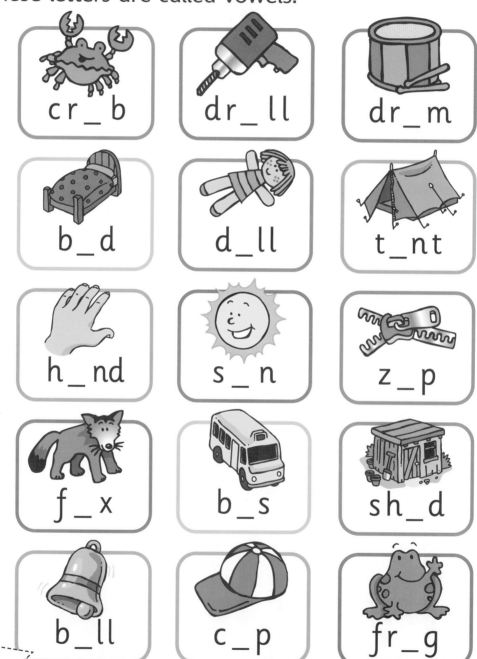

cr _ b

dr _ ll

dr _ m

b _ d

d _ ll

t _ nt

h _ nd

s _ n

z _ p

f _ x

b _ s

sh _ d

b _ ll

c _ p

fr _ g

Note for parent: This activity gives practice
with short vowels.

Right or wrong?

Cross out the wrong middle sound beside each picture. Complete each word using the correct middle sound.

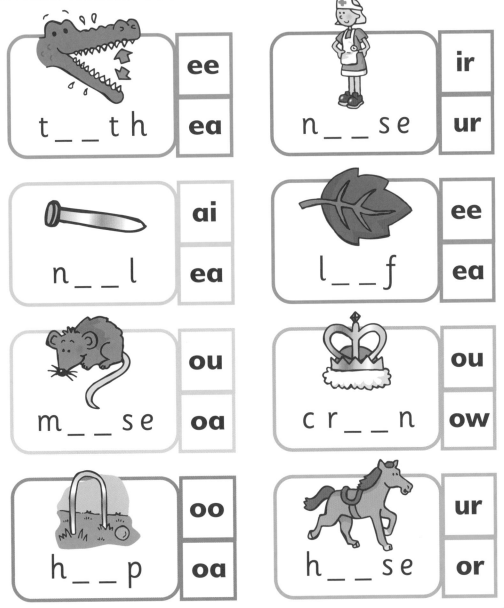

t _ _ th   ee / ea

n _ _ s e   ir / ur

n _ _ l   ai / ea

l _ _ f   ee / ea

m _ _ s e   ou / oa

c r _ _ n   ou / ow

h _ _ p   oo / oa

h _ _ s e   ur / or

Note for parent: This activity encourages children to listen to double sounds in the middle of words.

Making plurals

Complete the plural words below. Remember that plural means 'more than one'. If a word ends in **ss**, add **es** to make the plural.

princess = princesses

dress = _ _ _ _ _ _ _

glass = _ _ _ _ _ _ _

cross = _ _ _ _ _ _ _

If a word ends in **y**, take away the **y** and add **ies**.

baby = _ _ _ _ _ _

pony = _ _ _ _ _ _

lady = _ _ _ _ _ _

cherry = _ _ _ _ _ _ _

Note to parent: This activity gives practice with the plural forms es and ies.

Building words

Make four short words using the letters in each long one. Write the new words inside the balloons and then read them.

something

anyone

captain

heard

princess

Note for parent: This activity helps with word building.

Sound alike

Some words sound the same but have different spellings. Read the sentences. Cross out the words that are wrong.

I could not **see/sea** the moon.

I have **too/two** feet.

You can watch the stars at **knight/night**.

I had a **knew/new** bike for my birthday.

You can **right/write** a letter with my pen.

Can you write a sentence using each of these words?

way _____

_____

weigh _____

_____

Note to parent: This activity helps children to understand that some words sound the same but have different spellings.

Making new words

Say the name of each picture. Draw a line to join two pictures to make one word. Write the new words. You can use a dictionary to help you.

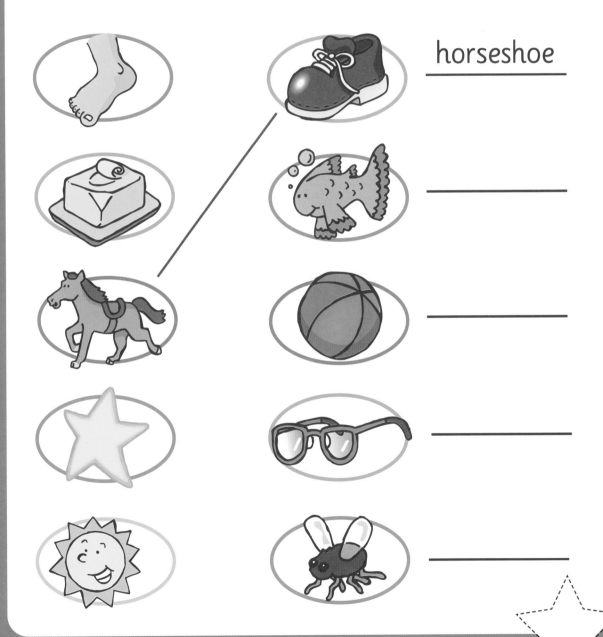

horseshoe

Note for parent: This activity helps children to make one word from two separate words.

Treble sounds

Read the beginning sounds. Draw a circle around two pictures that start in the same way.

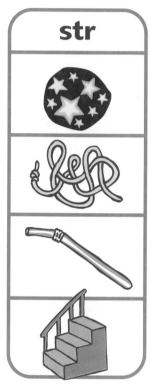

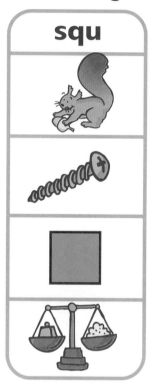

Read the sentences. Think of the missing word and complete it. Use a dictionary to help you.

I thr _ _ the ball in the air.

A small river is called a str _ _ _.

A mouse squ _ _ _ _.

Note to parent: This activity helps children to identify the treble beginning sounds thr, str and squ.

Opposites

What are the opposites of the words below?
Each answer is the opposite of the clue word. Fill in
the word grid. You can use a dictionary to help you.

ACROSS
1. little   4. light
2. cold   5. fat
3. open   6. clean

DOWN
1. dry   4. happy
2. front   5. full
3. new   6. low

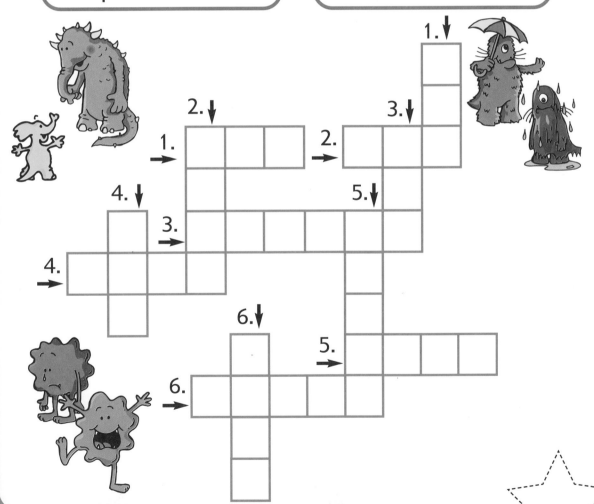

Note for parent: This activity helps children to learn
about opposites and gives practice with a dictionary.

Building words

Fill in the missing letters. The pictures will help you.

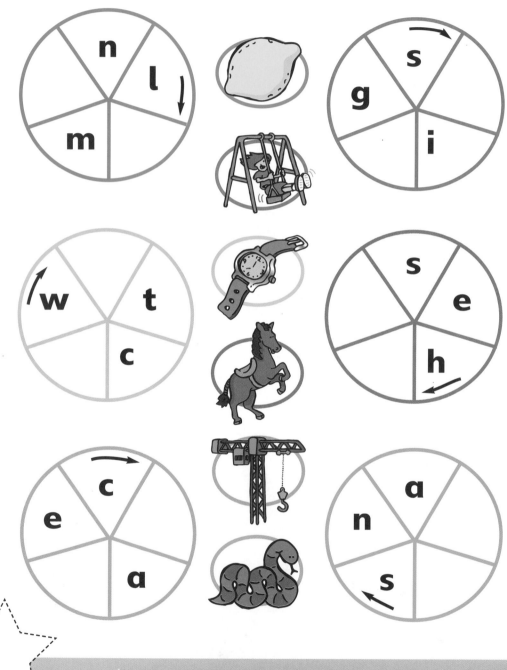

Note to parent: This activity gives practice with building and writing words.

Two together

Join two parts to make a word. Write the whole word and then draw a picture of it.

ch   arf   _____

sn   air   _____

sc   ail   _____

dr   umpet   _____

fl   um   _____

tr   ower   _____

Note for parent: This page encourages children to associate words and pictures.

Second chance

Complete the plural words below.
Add either **es** or **ies**.

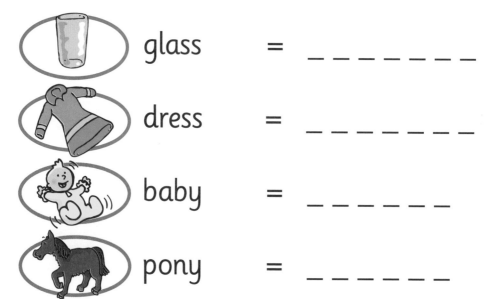

glass = _ _ _ _ _ _ _ _

dress = _ _ _ _ _ _ _ _

baby = _ _ _ _ _ _ _

pony = _ _ _ _ _ _ _

Fill in the missing letters. The pictures will help you.

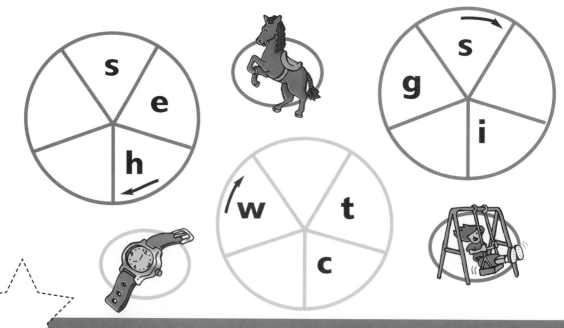

228

Note to parent: This activity is another chance to
see what children have remembered.

Dictionary practice

This is a page from a picture dictionary. Complete the missing parts. The first one has been done for you.

kennel	A kennel is a small house for a dog.
kettle	You can boil water in a kettle.
key	_____ _____
kite	A kite flies in the air. It is joined to a long piece of string.
kitten	_____ _____
knife	A knife is a sharp tool. You use a knife to cut your food.

Note for parent: This activity helps children to understand and use dictionary skills.

Rhyming words

Find a word in the balloon that rhymes with each word in the basket. Write the rhyming word in the basket.

made

tea   head

hare

meat

train

fly   wood

would _____		bed _____	
meet _____		maid _____	
hair _____		sigh _____	
me _____		plane _____	

Note for parent: This activity introduces rhyming words with a different spelling pattern.

Book titles

Look carefully at the pictures on the book covers. Make up a title for each book and write it on the cover. Colour the pictures.

 Note for parent: This activity encourages children to read and understand book titles.

Answers

Page 12
clockwise from top left: 8 spots, 10 spots, 6 spots, 4 spots, 7 spots, 9 spots.

Page 13
clockwise from left: frog 1 needs no extra spots, frog 2 needs 3 extra spots, frog 3 needs 1 extra spot, frog 4 needs 4 extra spots, frog 5 needs 5 extra spots, frog 6 needs 2 extra spots, frog 7 needs 6 extra spots.

Page 14
3 and 2 make 5 altogether, 2 and 4 make 6 altogether.
buttons: 1 + 6 = 7; stars: 4 + 3 = 7; sweets: 5 + 2 = 7; hearts: 6 + 3 = 9.

Page 15
3 + 5 = 8, 4 + 4 = 8, 1 + 5 = 6, 2 + 5 = 7.

Page 16
row 1: 4 take away 2 leaves 2; 6 take away 2 leaves 4; 5 take away 2 leaves 3.
row 2: 8 take away 2 leaves 6; 7 take away 2 leaves 5; 10 take away 2 leaves 8.
row 3: 3 – 2 = 1, 2 – 2 = 0, 9 – 2 = 7.

Page 17

Page 18

Page 20
row 1 are cubes; row 2 are cylinders, row 3 are spheres, row 4 are cuboids.

Page 21
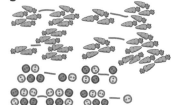

Page 22
 triangle, ◯ circle, ▭ rectangle, ☐ square.

Page 23
red bags = ✗; yellow bags = ✔.

Page 24
1 + 4 = 5, 3 + 3 = 6, 4 + 6 = 10.
4 + 6 = 10, 8 + 2 = 10.

Page 25
4 + 3 = 7, 2 + 5 = 7, 6 + 2 = 8, 3 + 3 = 6, 6 + 3 = 9, 1 + 5 = 6.
total of 4: red and yellow scarves; total of 6: orange and dark-blue scarves; total of 7: pink and bright-blue scarves; total of 10: green and purple scarves.

Page 26
4 – 2 = 2, 7 – 3 = 4, 8 – 5 = 3, 5 – 2 = 3, 7 – 4 = 3.

Page 27
4 – 1 = 3, 5 – 3 = 2, 8 – 7 = 1, 5 – 5 = 0, 9 – 5 = 4, 10 – 2 = 8. 10 – 5 and 5 – 0; 8 – 7 and 6 – 5; 10 – 7 and 6 – 3.

Page 28
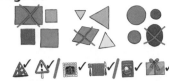

Page 29

rectangles, triangles, circles, squares

Page 30
11 o'clock, 8 o'clock, 5 o'clock.

Page 31

From left to right: half-past 4, half-past 10, half-past 7.

Page 32

Page 33
2 + 4 = 6, 3 + 3 = 6, 5 + 4 = 9, 6 + 4 = 10, 5 + 5 = 10, 2 + 3 = 5, 1 + 7 = 8, 2 + 7 = 9, 2 + 2 = 4.

10 – 1 = 9, 5 – 3 = 2, 4 – 2 = 2, 7 – 4 = 3, 6 – 5 = 1, 8 – 3 = 5, 9 – 6 = 3, 7 – 2 = 5, 10 – 6 = 4.

Page 34
Top train: 9, 10, 11, 12, 13, 14, 15, 16, 17. Middle train: 11, 12, 13, 14, 15, 16, 17, 18, 19, 20. Bottom train: 7, 8, 9, 10, 11, 12, 13, 14, 15, 16.
eleven–11, fourteen–14, twelve–12, fifteen–15, twenty–20, sixteen–16, thirteen–13, seventeen–17.

Page 35
clockwise from top left: rhinoceros, tiger, monkey, elephant.

Page 36
8 + 3 = 11, 9 + 5 = 14, 8 + 7 = 15, 6 + 7 = 13, 9 + 9 = 18, 6 + 4 = 10.
10 + 3 = 13, 10 + 5 = 15, 10 + 8 = 18, 10 + 6 = 16, 10 + 10 = 20, 10 + 1 = 11.

Page 37
12 – 8 = 4, 12 – 6 = 6, 13 – 4 = 9, 11 – 9 = 2, 16 – 8 = 8, 12 – 5 = 7.
20 – 4 = 16, 20 – 5 = 15, 20 – 6 = 14, 20 – 8 = 12, 20 – 2 = 18, 20 – 7 = 13.

Page 40

dog, fox, log;
hat, bat, fan;
bell, web, peg;
sum, jug, bus;
six, pig, lips.

Page 41

man, red, pig, sock, jet, duck, bus;
bed, log, fish, crab, men.

Page 42

Row 1: book; row 2: tree; row 3:
cat; row 4: house; row 5: bicycle.

Page 43

The teacher is under the table. ✗
A girl is reading a book. ✓
A boy is painting the door. ✗
The teacher is looking at the
children. ✓
A cat is reading a book. ✗
A boy has got a brush. ✓
The hamster is on its cage. ✗

Page 46

clock, bridge, crown, black;
green, plug, drill, flag.

Page 47

sp: spider, spoon, spanner;
st: stool, stamp, star;
sn: snail, snake, snowman;
sw: swan, switch, swing.

Page 48

cl – clown, dr – drum, sn – snail,
bl – blue, gr – grapes, sp – spider,
st – star, sw – swan.

Page 50

Everyone fell over and the turnip
came out. **D**
The farmer saw an enormous
turnip. **A**

Everyone tried to pull up the
turnip. **C**
The farmer tried to pull up the
turnip. **B**

Page 52

ball, dog, cat; bcd.
house, fish, girl; fgh.
ladybird, moon, key; klm.
rabbit, queen, parachute; pqr.
umbrella, seesaw, television; stu.

Page 53

or – fork, us – bus, an – man,
all – ball, am – lamb, in – twins,
at – bat.

Page 54

A little girl put on her dress.
The sun was hot.
I like getting into my bed to go to
sleep.
I can see a bird's nest in the tree.
Dad kicked the ball.
A little boy put on his football
boots.

Page 55

What is the time?
I like to eat chips.
When do I go to school?
The car was going fast.
Who went up the hill with Jill?
The cat likes to sit on my lap.

There are 8 capital letters.

Page 56

Alison, Duncan, Imran, Jamilla,
Meena, Patrick, Samuel, Wendy.

Page 57

Wednesday, Saturday, Thursday,
Friday, Sunday, Tuesday, Monday.

Page 59

9827, 9026, 9146, 9544.
Ms Walker
Mr Anderson
Mrs Todd
Mrs Depster

Page 60

elephant
A large animal with a long trunk
and ivory tusks. It lives in Africa
and Asia.

kangaroo
A large animal that can jump very
well. It carries its young in a pouch.
It comes from Australia.

monkey
A small animal with long arms
and feet that it uses like hands. It
lives in jungles.

panda
A black and white animal like a
bear. It lives in China.

zebra
An animal like a horse with black
and white stripes. It lives in Africa.

Page 61

giraffes, penguins, whales, bears,
turtles.
10, 4, 20, 18, 14.

Page 62

cl, br, cr, bl;
dr, gr, pl, fl.

spider›spade
snake›snail
swan›swing
star›stool

Page 63

Kitchen: pan / knife / frying pan /
spoon / food processor.
Garden: spade / wheelbarrow /
watering can / fork / lawnmower.

Answers

Pages 66–67

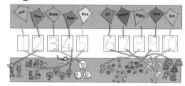

Page 68

Page 69

There is more than one possible answer. Parents need to check their child's answers for this page.

Pages 70–71

6 biscuits altogether, 6 cakes altogether, 5 pizzas altogether, 7 ice creams altogether, 9 sweets altogether.
3 and 2 make 5 altogether, 4 and 3 make 7 altogether, 6 and 2 make 8 altogether.

Page 72

5 take away 2 leaves 3, 6 take away 2 leaves 4, 8 take away 2 leaves 6, 4 take away 2 leaves 2, 9 take away 3 leaves 6.

Page 73

5 children, 4 chairs, difference = 1.
7 children, 5 chairs, difference = 2.
6 children, 3 chairs, difference = 3.

Pages 74–75

4 sweets add 2 sweets = 6 sweets;
6 sweets add 1 sweet = 7 sweets;
5 sweets add 3 sweets = 8 sweets;
7 sweets add 2 sweets = 9 sweets.
6 drinks take away 1 drink = 5 drinks;
5 drinks take away 3 drinks = 2 drinks;
3 drinks take away 2 drinks = 1 drink;
7 drinks take away 4 drinks = 3 drinks.

Page 76

6 biscuits altogether, 6 cakes altogether. 6 and 2 make 8 altogether. 8 take away 2 leaves 6, 4 take away 2 leaves 2.

Page 77

line 1: 2 rabbits are hidden,
line 2: 1 rabbit is hidden,
line 3: 4 rabbits are hidden,
line 4: 5 rabbits are hidden.

Pages 78–79

$2 + 3 = 5$, $3 + 4 = 7$, $4 + 5 = 9$.
$3 + 5 = 8$ altogether, $4 + 2 = 6$ altogether. $3 + 2 = 5$, $2 + 2 = 4$, $4 + 3 = 7$, $5 + 1 = 6$, $6 + 3 = 9$, $4 + 5 = 9$.

Pages 80–81

$7 - 2 = 5$, $5 - 2 = 3$, $8 - 2 = 6$.
Parents need to check child's answer for the last sum on page 80.
5 balls take away 3 balls = 2 balls,
4 balls take away 2 balls = 2 balls,
8 balls take away 4 balls = 4 balls.

Pages 82–83

$4 + 2 = 6$, $5 + 3 = 8$, $7 + 2 = 9$,
$3 + 4 = 7$, $6 + 4 = 10$, $2 + 3 = 5$.
$5 + 2 = 7$, $4 + 1 = 5$, $3 + 3 = 6$,
$6 + 3 = 9$, $3 + 1 = 4$.
The missing numbers are:
blue rocket – 6, 9, 10; green rocket – 1, 3, 4, 8; red rocket – 8, 9, 12, 15.

Pages 84–85

$6 - 3 = 3$, $5 - 2 = 3$, $8 - 4 = 4$,
$9 - 3 = 6$, $10 - 2 = 8$, $7 - 6 = 1$.

Pages 86–87

6: $0 + 6$, $1 + 5$, $2 + 4$. 8: $1 + 7$, $2 + 6$, $3 + 5$. 9: $1 + 8$, $2 + 7$, $3 + 6$.
7: $0 + 7$, $1 + 6$, $2 + 5$.

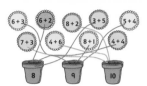

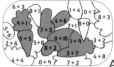
A rabbit and a carrot are hidden among the shapes.

Page 88

3: $4 - 1$, $7 - 4$, $3 - 0$, $9 - 6$, $8 - 5$.
4: $7 - 3$, $5 - 1$, $9 - 5$, $8 - 4$, $6 - 2$.
Possible answers are: $6 - 1$, $8 - 3$, $9 - 4$.

Page 89

5 balls take away 3 balls = 2 balls,
4 balls take away 3 balls = 1 ball.

Pages 90–91

$4 + 3 = 7$, $6 + 2 = 8$, $5 + 5 = 10$, $9 + 1 = 10$, $7 + 2 = 9$, $3 + 5 = 8$, $2 + 4 = 6$, $4 + 4 = 8$, $6 + 3 = 9$. The missing numbers are: row 1 – 6, 8. row 2 – 10, 9, 8, 10. $4 + 3 = 7$, $3 + 2 = 5$, $4 + 5 = 9$, $6 + 3 = 9$, $2 + 8 = 10$, $5 + 3 = 8$, $6 + 2 = 8$, $3 + 3 = 6$, $3 + 7 = 10$. The missing totals are: train 1 – 6, 9; train 2 – 3, 6, 8; train 3 – 3, 4, 7.

Pages 92–93

$6 - 4 = 2$, $7 - 3 = 4$, $5 - 1 = 4$,
$8 - 5 = 3$, $6 - 3 = 3$, $9 - 4 = 5$,
$10 - 5 = 5$, $7 - 4 = 3$, $8 - 3 = 5$.
The number 4 is hidden in the grid.

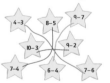

$7 - 4 = 3$, $6 - 2 = 4$, $5 - 3 = 2$,
$8 - 4 = 4$, $6 - 3 = 3$, $7 - 2 = 5$,
$9 - 6 = 3$, $9 - 5 = 4$, $10 - 4 = 6$.

Page 94–95
The missing letters are:
c f g i l
n r u x y .

Page 96
The missing letters are:
b c e g h j k m.

Page 97
carpet, toothbrush, shed,
telephone, caterpillar, fork, cup,
spoon, sheet, man.

Page 98
ball/wall, balloon/moon,
bee/tree, nail/snail, carrot/parrot.

Page 99
flag, dragon, clock, flower,
clown, spoon, grapes, drum.

Page 100
The missing letters are:
o r s u x y.

Page 101
tr–triangle, dr–drum, ch–chair,
gl–glove, cl–clock, br–brush,
cr–crayons, sc–scarf, fl–flowers,
bl–blanket.

Page 102
hat, sun, mop, net, pig, cup, van,
fox, six.

Page 103
The missing letters are:
c f.
dragon, clown, spoon.

Page 104
bat–cat, fox–box, jar–car,
dog–log.

Page 105
butterfly / but, fly; heart / art;
window / win; snail / nail;
hand / and; caterpillar / cat, ill.

Page 106
bridge/brick, skeleton/skier,
dragon/dress, grass/grapes,
clown/cloud.

Page 107
clock, slide, train, spider, twins,
frog.

Page 108
fish, egg, duck – def; ice cream,
horse, goat – ghi; key, lemon,
jellyfish – jkl; nurse, orange, moon
– mno.

Page 109

	f	r	o	g			
	l		r				
b	r	e	a	d	■		
	l			p	l	u	g
u			e			l	
e			s			o	
						b	
						e	

Page 110
bus, pig, bee, cup, saw, car.

Page 111
1. ship, 2. sheep, 3. shoes,
4. shark, 5. shell, 6. shorts.

Page 112
bus, dog, bat, drum, crab, fork,
cup, ten.

Page 113
Possible answers are:
cherries/chocolate, train/tractor,
straws/strawberries, swan/switch,
drum/drawing, crocodile/crayons.

Page 114

The animal is a dinosaur.

Page 115
ducks, pigs, cows, farmers, cats.

Page 116
sn: snail/snow/snake;
cr: crocodile/crayon/crab;
sp: spider/spade/spoon;
fl: fly/flower/flag.

Page 117
1. ship, 2. sheep, 3. shell.
cows, farmers, cats.

Page 118
str + ing = string, tr + ain =
train, bl + ack = black, gl + asses
= glasses, ch + erries = cherries,
scr + ew = screw.

Page 119
star/car, sock/duck, fish/brush,
dice/mice, switch/witch.

Page 120
cub/cube, pip/pipe, fir/fire,
cap/cape.

Page 121
transport: car/bus/train;
food: banana/bread/apple;
animals: tiger/giraffe/lion.

Answers

Pages 122–123

2+2=4, 3+4=7, 6+3=9, 3+5=8, 4+5 =9, 6+6=12. 5+5 and 6+4 (=10), 3+1 and 2+2 (=4), 5+2 and 6+1 (=7), 5+4 and 6+3 (=9). Odd one out is 6+5.
3+5=8, 2+8=10, 5+7=12, 7+4=11, 4+5=9. +2 machine: IN: 3, 0; OUT: 9, 6. +4 machine: IN: 6, 8; OUT: 6,8,9.

Page 124

9–3=6, 6–4=2. 9-6=3, 5-3=2, 12–7=5, 12–6=6, 10–6=4. No-one catches the fish 11–2.

Page 125

11–3=8, 10–3=7, 6–3=3, 5–3=2. 7–5=2, 12–5=7, 5–5=0, 9–5=4.

Pages 126–127

3+4=7, 7–5=2, 4+4=8, 12–6=6, 7+2=9, 6–6=0, 6+2=8, 11–3=8. 7–2=5, 3+5=8, 6+4=10, 7–7=0, 5+ or –0 =5, 0+6=6.
10–9=1, 10–2=8, 2+2=4, 12–3=9, 4+2=6, 7+3=10, 6+6=12. 8–8=0,10–5=5, 8–6=2, 5+2=7, 9+2=11, 5+4=9. The 3 star has no broomstick. The 9 star has two broomsticks (12–3=9, 5+4=9).

Page 128

10–ten, 20–twenty, 30–thirty, 40–forty, 50–fifty, 60–sixty, 70– seventy, 80–eighty, 90–ninety, 100–one hundred. 43, 58, 77, 30, 60, 90. Even numbers are: 42, 58, 76, 30, 60, 90. 45, 63, 84, 29, 49, 69. Odd numbers are: 45, 63, 85, 29, 49, 69.

Page 129

Above: red train 40, 41, 42, 43 ,44; green train 58, 59, 63, 64, 65; blue train 93, 94, 95, 96, 97.
Below: blue train 87, 86, 85, 84, 83; green train 69, 68, 64, 63, 62; red train 60, 59, 58, 57, 56.
Red numbers: 89, 87, 85, 83; 69, 67, 65, 63; 59, 57, 55, 53.
Yellow numbers: 90, 88, 86, 84; 68, 66, 64, 62; 60, 58, 56, 54.

Pages 130–131

Pentagons have 5 sides. Hexagons have 6 sides. Octagons have 8 sides.

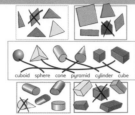

Page 132

Missing numbers (from left to right): 3, 3, 6,; 5, 4, 4,; 3, 6, 0,; 8, 3, 8. Odd numbers to be coloured are: 13, 33, 49, 65, 81, 85. Shape names are: triangle, pentagon, hexagon, cone, cylinder, pyramid.

Page 133

7+5=12, 9+11=20, 8+3=11, 10+8=18, 6+8=14, 8+9=17. Red spaceships are: 6+8, 6+4, 6+6, 9+9, 8+8, 7+7, 10+10.

Pages 134–135

12–9=3, 16-5=11, 13-8=5, 14-7=7, 15-6=9, 17-9=8, 12-8=4, 15-9=6, 19-9=10, 11-9=2. The eggs 15–6 and 14–9 are the odd ones out.
The missing numbers are: 8, 11, 9, 13; 6, 9, 11, 15; 3, 6, 14, 18. The difference is (from left to right): 9, 9, 13; 5, 6, 4.

Page 136

Mystery numbers are 11 and 15.

Page 137

Red fish: 7 + 0 (= 7); yellow fish: 9 – 5 (= 4).

Pages 138–139

Page 140

Missing numbers are (from left to right): Top: 5, 1, 4; 6, 9, 3; 9, 2, 5. Middle:10, 30, 70; 20, 40, 80; 20, 50, 90. Bottom: 13=10+3, 43=40+3, 62=60+2, 26=20+6, 48=40+8, 75=70+5.

Page 141

47, 74; 49, 43, 67; 44, 61, 79; 18, 27, 42.

Pages 142–143

6.00, 6.15, 6.30, 6.45, 7.00.

Page 144

Difference is 4, 14, 4. 12+8, 12–6, 15+3, 18+12, and 15+11 should be coloured. Missing numbers (from left to right): 6, 8, 9, 30, 60, 80.

Page 145

Blue train: 8,10,12,14,16,18,20. Hidden numbers (from left to right): 3, 5, 8; 10, 2, 7; 1, 9, 6. Red train: 40, 50, 60, 70, 80, 90, 100. Hidden numbers (from left to right): 3, 6, 2; 4, 9, 10; 8, 1.

Page 146

Missing numbers are: 20, 25, 30, 35, 40, 45, 50. Hidden numbers are (from left to right): 1, 3, 9; 5, 6, 2; 8, 4, 7. Left: 3 fives; right: 6 fives.

Page 147

Page 148

top row: 3 balls; middle row: 3 balls; bottom row: 2 balls.

Page 149

parrots: 2 twos and 3 twos; ducks: 3 threes and 4 threes; marbles: 3 fours, 2 fours and 4 fours.

Page 151

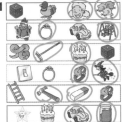

Page 152

1. The boy is reading a book.
2. The girl is looking at the television.
3. The dog is playing with a ball.
4. The man is cutting the grass.

Some of the nouns are:
1. sofa, lamp, mug, shoes.
2. slippers, book, video.
3. tree, house, grass.
4. lawnmower, flowers, boots, hat.

Page 153

1. A ladybird is very small. 2. The leaves fell off the tree because it was windy. 3. The sun was shining and the sky was blue. 4. Dad had just picked the flowers so they were fresh. 5. The dog was happy because he had a new ball. 6. It was cold in the garden and there was ice on the pond.

Page 154-155

Page 156

fog = frog; coot = coat; aple = apple; lam = lamb; bred = bread; baloon = balloon; pair = pear; qeen = queen.

Page 157

boy = A male child. **hutch** = A pet rabbit's home. **monster** = A creature you read about in fairy tales. **saw** = A tool that has sharp metal teeth. **penguin** = A black-and-white bird that cannot fly.

Page 158

top: sleeping, licking.
middle: running, climbing.
bottom: swimming, flying.

Page 159

two–2, six–6, three–3, eight–8, ten–10, four–4, seven–7, nine–9, one–1, five–5.

er   ce   ake   ar   tch   ing

Page 160

1. November. 2. January.
3. October. 4. July. 5. September.
6. May and December.

Page 161

leaf, snail, peach, seal, pail, seat. boat, mouse, coat, cloud, road, trousers.

Page 162

Possible answers are:
Dad is playing with a red ball.
The baby is eating a big ice cream.
The brown dog is chasing the cat.
Mum is feeding the hungry ducks.

Page 163

starfish, waterfall, homework, playtime, toothbrush, football, earring, bookmark.

Page 164

bear – pear – wear; fire – wire – hire; jaw – claw – straw; brown – clown – crown; flight – bright – knight.

Page 165

1. Kelly and Sam; 2. Sam and Anna; 3. Kelly and Anna; 4. Kelly and Anna; 5. Sam and Anna; 6. Kelly and Anna.

Page 166

1. Parrot said, "I like to fly and sing." 2. Monkey said, "I have a long tail." 3. Horse said, "I like to eat hay." 4. Kangaroo said, "I like to jump and hop." 5. Elephant said, "I have a long trunk."

Page 167

is not = isn't; cannot = can't;

I would = I'd; I am = I'm; will not = won't; you have = you've.

I'd like to see you but I'm ill. I can't go out but I'd like to see you if you have time and it's not too far for you to come.

Page 171

1. silly; 2. sensible; 3. silly; 4. silly; 5. silly; 6. sensible.

Page 172

1. May; 2. shape; 3. paint; 4. lion; 5. man. Shapes = square, triangle, circle, rectangle. Farm animals = sheep, horse, pig, cow. Vehicles = bus, car, lorry, van. Days of week = Monday, Friday, Tuesday, Sunday. Colours = red, orange, blue, green.

Page 173

is not = isn't; I would = I'd; cannot = can't. Nouns: dog, mouse, tree. Verbs: grows, run, squeaks. Adjectives = tall, soft, cold.

Page 174

1. wet–dry; 2. soft–hard; 3. first–last; 4. far–near; 5. empty–full; 6. hot–cold; 7. night–day; 8. push–pull; 9. short–long; 10. heavy–light.

Page 175

1. The dog barked at the burglar.
2. The horse galloped across the field. 3. The frog jumped out of the pond. 4. The birds flew into the air. 5. The spider spun a big web.
6. The cat slept on the wall.

Page 176

a	e	m	c	i	g	r	t	h	j
s	r	l	c	b	t	a	l	q	k
d	o	g	s	g	r	o	w	s	z
f	k	t	m	u	e	s	b	g	s
d	g	s	t	e	q	n	q	u	
r	u	n	s	u	f	u	d	m	p
p	x	o	l	j	y	e	u	o	n
w	f	l	o	o	v	a	l	u	t
y	a	z	e	v	n	k	y	s	b
t	h	x	a	e	c	s	w	e	d

Page 177

Some of the words you can make are: or, let, is, as, pea, at, mat, me. man/pan; coat/boat; robber/rubber; card/cart; fork/fort; wolf/golf.

Answers

Pages 178–179

4 + 5 = 9, 6 + 4 = 10, 3 + 5 = 8,
5 + 5 = 10

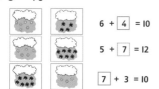

6 + [4] = 10

5 + [7] = 12

[7] + 3 = 10

4 + 8 = 12, 3 + 9 = 12, 7 + 5 = 12,
6 + 6 = 12.

Pages 180–181

6 – 4 = 2, 9 – 4 = 5, 10 – 4 = 6,
12 – 4 = 8.
7 – 5 = 2, 9 – 5 = 4, 12 – 5 = 7,
11 – 5 = 6.
12 – 3 = 9, 9 – 1 = 8, 8 – 5 = 3,
3 – 2 = 1.

Page 182

12 + 3 = 15, 8 + 4 = 12, 7 + 7 = 14,
9 + 6 = 15, 11 + 5 = 16.

Page 183

14 – 5 = 9, 18 – 6 = 12, 16 – 7 = 9.
10 – 4 = 6, 13 – 5 = 8, 11 – 3 = 8,
14 – 6 = 8, 12 – 4 = 8,
15 – 6 = 9, 17 – 4 = 13, 16 – 3 = 13.

Pages 184–185

4 + 7 = 11, 8 + 5 = 13, 6 + 9 = 15.
+ 9 machine: 7 + 9 = 16, 4 + 9 = 13,
8 + 9 = 17, 5 + 9 = 14, 9 + 9 = 18.
– 7 machine: 12 – 7 = 5, 9 – 7 = 2,
15 – 7 = 8, 13 – 7 = 6, 10 – 7 = 3.
– 9 machine: 11 – 9 = 2, 14 – 9 = 5,
12 – 9 = 3, 18 – 9 = 9, 16 – 9 = 7.

Pages 186–187

The difference between 3 and 7 is 4.
The difference between 5 and 11 is 6.
The difference between 6 and 10 is 4.
The difference between 7 and 12 is 5.
The difference between 9 and 4 is 5.
The difference between 6 and 11 is 5.

yellow boat: 9, red boat: 5 or 15,
purple boat: 8, blue boat: 4 or 14.

Page 188

Total of 9: 4 + 5, 7 + 2, 6 + 3, 8 + 1.
Total of 12: 4 + 8, 5 + 7, 6 + 6, 9 + 3.

Page 189

5 + 5 = 10. 6 – 4 = 2, 10 – 4 = 6.

Pages 190–191

9 + 9 = 18, 6 + 5 = 11, pea. 12 +
8 = 20, 11 + 7 = 18, 8 + 3 = 11, 7 +
7 = 14, bean. 7 + 5 = 12, 2 + 9 = 11,
10 + 7 = 17, 8 + 9 = 17, 9 + 6 =
15, 10 + 9 = 19, carrot. 8 + 8 = 16,
11 + 4 = 15, 12 + 7 = 19, 6 + 5 =
11, 5 + 14 = 19, 8 + 7 = 15, potato.

The missing numbers are:
top: 10, 13, 20; middle: 4, 10, 12,
20; bottom: 7, 8, 14, 20.

Pages 192–193

5: 12 – 7, 9 – 4, 13 – 8, 11 – 6.
6: 10 – 4, 11 – 5, 9 – 3, 14 – 8.
15 – 8 = 7, 17 – 9 = 8, 14 – 6 = 8,
13 – 9 = 4, 11 – 4 = 7, 12 – 8 = 4.
The odd ones out are: top left:
18 – 9, top right: 14 – 8, centre:
17 – 13, 13 – 9 and 11 – 7, 14 – 8
and 12 – 6, 15 – 8 and 13 – 6.

Pages 194–195

14 – 7 = seven, 11 – 6 = five,
13 – 7 = six, 17 – 5 = twelve,
13 – 5 = eight, 16 – 15 = one,
16 – 7 = nine. Mystery number = sixteen.
9 – 4 = 5, 8 – 7 = 1, 11 – 6 = 5, 7 – 5
= 2, 10 – 7 = 3.
12 – 6 = 6, 7 – 4 = 3, 15 – 10 = 5, 9 –
6 = 3, 11 – 4 = 7.
8 – 4 = 4, 13 – 8 = 5, 6 – 2 = 4,
10 – 5 = 5, 14 – 7 = 7.
Blue see-saw: 9 and 5, green see-
saw: 8 and 8, yellow see-saw: 7
and 13. The missing numbers are:
dog: 11, 5; pig: 17, 13, 6; hen: 18,
15, 7.

Page 196

The missing totals are (from left to
right): 11, 13, 12.
The missing numbers are (from left
to right): 5, 3, 7.
The total in the centre is 20.

Page 197

Green purse: 20p; pink purse: 18p.
Box 1: £12; box 2: £11; box 3: £16.

Pages 198

4 + 4 = 8, 6 + 6 = 12, 3 + 3 = 6, 5 +
5 = 10, 8 + 8 = 16, 2 + 2 = 4, 7 + 7
= 14, 10 + 10 = 20, 9 + 9 = 18. 3 + 4
= 7, 5 + 6 = 11, 8 + 9 = 17, 10 + 9 =
19, 5 + 4 = 9, 6 + 7 = 13, 8 + 7 = 15.

Pages 199

The change from 20p is: 13p, 12p,
8p, 5p.

apple – 9p change, banana – 6p
change, lemon – 14p change, orange
– 11p change, pineapple – 4p change.

Page 200

8 + 3 = 11, 9 – 4 = 5, 7 + 6 = 13,
8 + 7 = 15, 12 – 6 = 6, 10 – 7 = 3,
12 – 3 = 9, 8 + 4 = 12.

Pages 201

The missing numbers are: top: 10,
13, 20; bottom: 4, 10, 12, 20. The
odd ones out are: left: 17 – 9, right:
18 – 9. banana – 6p change, apple
– 9p change, lemon – 14p change.

Pages 202–203

The missing numbers are: top: 50,
70, 80, 90, 110; bottom: 100, 130,
140, 160, 170.
7 + 2 = 9, 70 + 20 = 90; 4 + 3 = 7,
40 + 30 =70; 3 + 5 = 8, 30 + 50 =
80; 6 + 5 = 11, 60 + 50 = 110.
90 + 60 = 150, 70 + 70 = 140,
50 + 80 = 130, 50 + 70 = 120,
60 + 30 = 90, 70 + 40 = 110.

Page 204

wa<u>ll</u>/be<u>ll</u>, so<u>ck</u>/clo<u>ck</u>, <u>r</u>ing/s<u>w</u>ing,
hamme<u>r</u>/ladd<u>er</u>.

Page 205

well, lock, king, letter.

Page 206

star, scarf, barn, shark, card.

Page 207

cub/cube, cap/cape.
mice/dice, cake/lake, nose/rose,
tube/cube. There are other
possible answers.

Page 208

elephant: hat, tea, ant, help, let, leap, net.

aeroplane: plane, plan, an, leap, rope, ran, pan, pea, pear. You may find more words.

Page 209

Page 210

web, hat, cat, fox, bed, egg, sun, owl.

1. bed 2. cat 3. egg 4. fox 5. hat 6. owl 7. sun 8. web

Page 211

h<u>oo</u>k, c<u>oo</u>k, t<u>ee</u>th, b<u>oo</u>k, ch<u>ee</u>se, tr<u>ee</u>, f<u>oo</u>t, gr<u>ee</u>n.

m<u>oo</u>n, f<u>ee</u>t.

Page 212

row 1: nail, boat, coat;
row 2: goat, sail, tail;
row 3: snail, chain, soap, rain, toast.

Page 213

tall/ball, bees/trees, log/frog, string/swing, skate/gate, bite/kite.

Page 214

spoon, pea, snail, coat.

Page 215

wa<u>ll</u>/be<u>ll</u>, so<u>ck</u>/clo<u>ck</u>, ri<u>ng</u>/swi<u>ng</u>.
h<u>oo</u>k, c<u>oo</u>k, t<u>ee</u>th.

Page 216

bri<u>ck</u>s: du<u>ck</u>s, chi<u>ck</u>s; <u>k</u>ing: string, ring; wa<u>tch</u>: wi<u>tch</u>, swi<u>tch</u>; whis<u>tle</u>: cas<u>tle</u>, bot<u>tle</u>; dre<u>ss</u>: gla<u>ss</u>, gra<u>ss</u>.

Page 217

row 1: ch, fl, sw; row 2: cr, pl, sw; row 3: fl, br, cr; row 4: br, ch, pl.

Page 218

cr<u>a</u>b, dr<u>i</u>ll, dr<u>u</u>m; b<u>e</u>d, d<u>o</u>ll, t<u>e</u>nt; h<u>a</u>nd, s<u>u</u>n, z<u>i</u>p; f<u>o</u>x, b<u>u</u>s, sh<u>e</u>d; b<u>e</u>ll, c<u>a</u>p, fr<u>o</u>g.

Page 219

t<u>ee</u>th, n<u>ur</u>se, n<u>ai</u>l, l<u>ea</u>f, m<u>ou</u>se, cr<u>ow</u>n, h<u>oo</u>p, h<u>or</u>se.

Page 220

dresses, glasses, crosses; babies, ponies, ladies, cherries.

Page 221

something = some/thing/in/tin;
anyone = any/one/on/an;
captain = cap/pin/pan/can.
heard = he/red/hear/ear;
princess = prince/in/price/nice.
You may find other words.

Page 222

see, two, night, new, write.

Page 223

football, butterfly, starfish, sunglasses.

Page 224

thr: throne, three; str: string, straw; squ: squirrel, square.

I threw the ball in the air.

A small river is called a stream.

A mouse squeaks.

Page 225

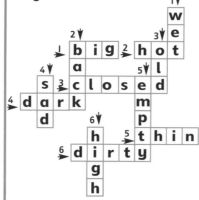

Page 226

lemon, swing, watch, horse, crane, snake.

Page 227

ch + air = chair, sn + ail = snail, sc + arf = scarf, dr + um = drum, fl + ower = flower, tr + umpet = trumpet.

Page 228

glasses, dresses, babies, ponies. horse, swing, watch.

Page 230

would/wood, meet/meat, hair/hare, me/tea, bed/head, maid/made, sigh/fly, plane/train.

The End